C. H.

# Cecil Hemley

# DIMENSIONS OF MIDNIGHT

## *Poetry & Prose*

***** * ****

EDITED BY ELAINE GOTTLIEB

WITH A FOREWORD BY

MARK VAN DOREN

OHIO UNIVERSITY PRESS

ATHENS, OHIO

Acknowledgment is made to the following in which some of the works included in this volume originally appeared: THE NEW MEXICO QUARTERLY, SATURDAY REVIEW, FRESCO and POETRY IN CRYSTAL (Steuben Glass Co.)

I am grateful to Farrar, Straus & Giroux (Noonday Press) for permission to reprint PORPHYRY'S JOURNEY and IN THE MIDNIGHT WOOD.

# FOREWORD

Cecil Hemley, who was primarily a poet, was also in the course of his too brief life a publisher, an editor, and a writer of fiction. Furthermore, he was a person. He was a generous, warm-spirited person whom none of his friends will forget. They will continue to hear his resonant, deep voice; they will continue to think of his remarkable eyes, so dark, so large, so eager with good will. They will remember these things because there is a connection between them and the kind of poet he was. The power in the person is a key to the power his poetry possesses, and possesses more than ever now that it is collected here.

Generosity, eagerness, good will: these are there, plus something that is much more difficult to name or define. Sadness would be the wrong name, and so would pain, though both suggest themselves. Perhaps there is no way—no prose way—to put into words the sense he so persistently had of belonging to two worlds that were infinitely apart. They were the world of idea and the world of fact; the world of innocence and the world of experience; the world of God and the world of man; the world imagined and the world found. These worlds confront each other in most of his poems; and the confrontation is moving. Nor is it ever as simple as the foregoing sentences might seem to make it sound. For one thing, Cecil Hemley had worked his way through to a position where he could love both worlds. The world of accident, of things as they are, was finally forgiven, even while the shining, the perfect world was not forgotten. The result is a kind of reality seldom encountered in the poetry of our time: a reality that glows beneath and through the always welcome clarity of the lines.

Many of the poems are memories of things lost, and sometimes—so thinks the wiser man—well lost. Yet not always so; for certain things that are lost forever would have been wonderful to keep, were such a consummation possible. As it is, they can only be remembered: cherished as childish things which the race itself has tragically put away. For the loss is more than personal, and indeed, if it were merely that, it would be of little interest. Cecil Hemley's distinction in the end is that he speaks for all thoughtful persons, for all minds that feel. If he is a changeling, so is each one of us. "We who have watched a golden age turn bronze"—he includes us too. The "tumult of insistent fact" is something he expects us to understand exactly as he does, just as he knows we "seek a spring beyond the spring." "The filth of time"—now those are hard words, but he counts on us to be Neoplatonists like him, veritable Porphyrys in fact, and hence incapable of being shocked. For he is going to tell us that time has its cleanness too: it obliterates what ought to be obliterated. "Some worlds are best left buried." "Some faiths should be lost." Some Odysseys are "fraudulent." We have to come to terms with time—"Peace, then, is possible."

The poetry of Cecil Hemley is serious, for it deals with great matters, and chiefly this one which a few of his own words have been called on to define. It is a subject of which he never lost sight, whether in his latest poems—witness "The Conflagration," "August Storm," "Little Elegy," "The Gentle Women," "The Betrayal" —or in his stories (especially "The Woman with Hysterical Eyes") or in the play about the swami who confronts our West and finds it wanting because it does not know how to live at the foot of the mountain from which he has descended. It is even in the two pieces of criticism here collected: the essay on fiction and the lecture on Isaac Bashevis Singer, whom it was Cecil

Hemley's chief glory as a publisher to have brought forward as his genius deserved. No act of his was more generous, more eager, more beautiful in its good will.

*Mark Van Doren*

# CONTENTS

xi

## *Prose*

### SHORT STORIES

xiv

XV

# Poetry
* * * * *

# FROM *In the Midnight Wood*

## Winter Night

Draw the curtains tight
This winter night.
Young lovers go unchilled
    Through frost and ice.
But we who've had our world
    Must lose the voice
Of tortured boughs and dead twigs hurled
    Against the windowpane
    With sleet and rain.

Come bring a book and we shall read aloud.
October's red becomes this silver shroud;
    But spring still sings
        For Guinevere,
    And Launcelot lusts
        Beside the mere,
        And will although we are not there
To know his violent wanderings.

Remember how our childhood caught
The passion of such tales if not the thought,
   And all the crimes,
      And all the grief
   Were songs of joy
      We thought too brief.
On some cold night like this the queen
   Her lover dead
Must have dreamed
      Of sins unravelled and the pure
      Light of her mind safe and secure.

          No, that we never read.
          That was left unsaid.

# Fallen Crescent

Here is a dull moon drifting on the sea,
     A sick moon,
     Washed by brine.
  It is myself I see.
This fallen crescent speaks to me
     With the tired tongue
     Of one no longer young.
  It is a waning moon,
     Staring into eternity,
     Alone, alone,
Mourning the endless circles it has flown
     Down opal cloudways
     That now are dark with storm.
  This is a fogging moon,
     Becoming stone,
     A sombre red of sorrow,
  Burning on the waves,
     Then gone.

# The Crazy One

In the maple tree outside my door,
All others flown, one gray bird stays,
Endlessly singing his repertoire,
    A single phrase.

Something is wrong, this crazy one
Bides past his hour; his weather eye
Should show him a cold, declining sun,
    And storm in the sky.

I have gone to the foot of the tree,
And shaken the boughs; off he goes,
Circling the garden, then stubbornly
    The strong wings close.

Go away bird! I fear your death
Here in my garden. If you care
To sing when winter holds the earth,
    Rebel elsewhere.

Sensible bird, now you are gone,
I rake the leaves; the autumn's done.
Here is one madcap I need not mourn,
    Would there were none.

# Witnesses

Once quiet meant discord and pain;
My frantic mind willed hurricane
To blow away its disbelief,
But violence brought it no relief.
How does it happen that a bough
In winter stillness calms me now?

The spirit sees what it has known;
It prints its trials on leaf and stone.
So leaf and stone record for me
The ways I went unwittingly.
What did I find? What do I know
That makes the silence beckon so?

## Eurydice

If anyone would rescue me,
He must descend into the cold;
He must disdain divinity,
The tideless sea in which I drowned.

If anyone would have me be,
As once a lover did of old,
He too must dare absurdity,
And walk the dark ways of a wound.

I seek a hero; but no one
Has faith to find me in the night,
And bear me upwards to the sun;
I am a name beyond time's fate.

I am a dream that lies unwon
With multitudes who also wait.

# The Beggar

Whose shadow follows me has found
My way of silence, and his wound
Is angry footfalls on the ground.

His servile protest, inward grown,
Becomes a menace to my bone;
Our shadows touch upon the stone.

Chance shadow, yet not chance the pain
That eats into that shadow's brain:
For it is shadow and must wane.

Our shadows merge, and then unfold,
His shadow, derelict and old,
Mine shivering from the final cold.

Should I leap from my core of fright,
And leave my shadow in the light,
Would I draw substance from the night?

# The Hero

Was it a horn that woke me?
I remembered a promise I had sworn,
How many ages ago I do not know.
Or was it spring breaking through bone
And the mail I had worn?

I have awakened, ready for battle;
I have returned.
I have slipped from the night
And with lance in my hand
I will fight for my own.

O comrades you do not answer.
I am alone
With rusting armor and blunted spears.
The day enters our cave.
But you whom I trusted are not here.

The miracle is possible;
I am achieved of air.
I have heard the cry of the suffering.
Do you not hear?
Now is our moment; you also swore.

No, no. This lance is shadow. I am no more
Than you silent sleepers,
Lost beyond the sun.
This too is slumber. I have not awakened.
I still await the sounding of the horn.

# The Conquerors

Who will remember what armies were here,
Or praise our incursions from north and south?
Babylon burns! It is we who despair.
Babylon conquered and an end of youth.

What did we seek, the battalions that came
Over the mountains? Why did we leave
Forest and valley to bring her to shame?
Babylon dies, and it is we who grieve.

The river will flow, the city not there;
The long caravans move deep into drought.
The ruins remain. We have ashes to share.
The gardens are dust. The sun has gone out.

This victory night the jackals scream.
Only the hot brazen silence is real.
Babylon lost, there is little to dream,
Little to wish for and nothing to feel.

White city, rise from the desert again,
Unjust, improper, be mistress, we slave,
Illumine the heavens, indolent, vain.
O cockatoos laugh. O courtesans save.

# My Absent God

My absent God does not disown
That timeless joy He lives alone;
He does not seek as once His own.

But should He change and dive from night
As swan or eagle, would the might
Of creature wings give me insight?

Would loving talons rip despair,
And make the ways of violence clear?
Would holy eyes their vision share?

Or if again, a bush in flame,
He burned into my brain His name,
Would I accept this Stranger's claim?

# Christmas Morning

Lord! Lord! Lord!
    My Asiatic king,
  The man upon the cross,
  That night from which I spring;
Where are you, then, my source?
  Again the church bells ring,
But I must walk abhorred,
  Unsure of anything.

Grace! Grace! Grace!
    Must I remain uncured,
  When children see your smile,
  And thieves have won reward?
You flee from me in guile,
  Abjuring and abjured,
Yet slumber in your place,
  Eternally adored.

# If He Were Anywhere

I would be His if He were anywhere;
If He were anything He would appear.

If He had any name the name I give
Would find Him in the night and make Him live.

But He is nameless, nothing, and nowhere,
Beyond concern with me and my despair.

And, naming Him, I only name my wish:
To break from bone and live in spirit's flesh.

And, seeking Him, still trammeled in the mind,
I dare not leave my selfish name behind.

That which is actual does not endure;
He will not have me till I forfeit more.

# He Must Be Born Again

Again that weary day when He must share
The wickedness of men who do not spare
Him birth. See now they penetrate His will,
Petitioners who fear the twilight's chill.

He must be born again; time needs His pain;
The ignorant must see the loved one slain.
They doubted Him—away—but His return
Will make them rage and He must hang or burn.

Midday nativity! and God's defiled,
And placed within the body of a child.
Mad sacrilege to crowd Him into bone,
And treat Him as a thing that space can own.

O Virgin, God is sucking at your breast,
But He will bring you little joy or rest.
O wise men, now divinity is here,
He has no Word to make His meaning clear.

# Furious Birds

Furious birds scream for the tropic sun,
Here in this birdhouse, dream, dream in their cries,
Dream of the jungles they have never seen.
Forever captives, yet they know the skies
Meant for their wings; their savage bodies rise
In ancient rhythms they have learned from night;
Deep in their veins the rushing river sighs,
The sudden dawn erupts in orange light.
Mad birds can dream, and dreams will serve as sight;
Wish is for them a witness and a truth.
The trees are there, the heavens in their height,
No cage deludes them for their will is south.
What dreaming birds foretell no man will see
Until he wakes to dream their mystery.

# Departure

Now she weighs anchor and departs the bay,
Red running lights and green against the gray.
Where are the harbors that my childhood knew,
And where the ships that journeyed to and fro?

Her way is east, but she will never find
Those spray-born cities living in my mind.
Where are the crews who knew to sail beyond
The edges of the sea which now surround?

The ships are sunk, the crews are long since dead;
The charts that guided them cannot be read.
Lost are the trade routes that once led to joy,
The crooked streets I wandered as a boy.

There still are wharves, but not such happy stir;
No mystery past beacons; gulls still soar.
But harbors that ships reach I seek to leave,
Dark, tired purlieus where the heart must grieve.

Beyond the jetty, almost out of sight,
She steams a silver shadow on the night.
Farewell swift voyager, for I too sail;
My ship drives forward and the shore lights pale.

I travel sea lanes limitless as thought,
And as you disappear, the towns I sought
Rise from the drifting waves; and round me move
The ghosts of lies, still closest to my love.

# Shadow Play

Now I have tracked you here, and you at bay,
All your disguises torn from you, I see
The shadow of a shadow. I am free
Of this which was not love but shadow play.
Shadow I will keep you locked from day,
My next love shall not be some shape of you,
An old confusion risen out of vanity,
To walk abroad and be untrue, untrue.
Love need not love old love; love can be new!
Beyond itself can reach another's sight.
When shadows leave themselves they penetrate
Past body's shadow, and there all is light.
There even mist must burn, and black turn white,
And any shadow is an angel's weight.

# At the Lake
*after Adam Mickiewicz*


Within their silent, perfect glass,
The mirror waters, vast and clear,
Reflect the silhouette of rocks,
Dark faces brooding on the shore.

Within their silent, perfect glass,
The mirror waters show the sky;
Clouds skim across the mirror's face,
And dim its surface as they die.

Within their silent, perfect glass,
The mirror waters image storm;
They glow with lightning, but the blasts
Of thunder do not mar their calm.

These mirror waters, as before,
Still lie in silence, vast and clear.

They mirror me, I mirror them,
As true a glass as they I am;
And as I turn away I leave
The images that gave them form.

Dark rocks must menace from the shore,
And thunderheads grow large with rain;

Lightning must flash above the lake,
And I must mirror and pass on,
Onward and onward without end.

# Eumenides

Their faces, involuted fear,
Their willful persons formed to act
Emotions they no longer share,

They do their chore with strictest tact,
The haunters who return to weep
Tears, time and death have made abstract.

Eumenides who ever keep
The tally that they have forgot.
Their admonitions fever sleep,

Their venom speeds the spirit's rot,
For they are worldlings past the grave,
Concerned with crime and counterplot.

The error is to think they save;
Ours is the power. Love forgave.

# In the Midnight Wood

When the moon shone,
And all was stone
In the midnight wood,
I understood.

In that sallow light,
I touched the night,
Without, within,
Its ancient skin.

When a cloud came,
It wrote my name
On the dark sky,
For it was I.

It snuffed the moon,
And there was none;
But two nights twined
Beneath the mind.

# It Has Occurred Before

The mold is there, you only need to pour,
And it will take not merely gold but brass;
It has occurred, it has occurred before.

There have been instances of bright allure
Where all the matter was composed of gas;
The mold is there, you only need to pour.

The prizes wait you and your fame is sure;
Demand is for the product in the mass.
It has occurred, it has occurred before.

For who will have the leisure to explore,
And find you are a mimic and an ass;
The mold is there, you only need to pour.

Perhaps your villanelle will not endure,
But even Wystan H's verse may pass;
It has occurred, it has occurred before.

It is the moment you are looking for;
To be the current leader of the class.
The mold is there, you only need to pour.
It has occurred, it has occurred before.

# Class Reunion

Those paunches and those tired pouchy eyes,
The standard baggage of the old come back
To watch the team perform and later elegize
In overheated dorms the quarterback
Who raced down sidelines twenty years ago
(What hips he had, oh how that boy could go);
Those relics, boring as the latest book,
As common as its style, crude as its plot,
Are not yourself, the flabby hands you shook
Are not your hands. No doubt all bodies rot,
And you are not the clean, the affable, the young,
But your tears fell not when the hymn was sung,
"Dear college, dear." Nor did you rise to cheer
The digits of your class. What had it done,
Its best an actor and a millionaire?
Old Thirty-four. Insurance men, a ton
Of prep school teachers, preachers, second-string
Executives and lawyers. This was man
Less than the angels. But then, sauntering
About the campus, studying the plan
Of the new gymnasium, your doubts began.

Your shadow slipped from you, stretched on the ground;
You traced its silhouette, and there you found

Your middle age. Did irony avail
To shrink the waistline, keep the kidneys sound?
But oh the mind! Was it not trim and hale,
Adventurous and strong, still striding down
The avenues of search as in its youth?
Fastidious would it take less than truth?
Ah truth! Day's image of you on the grass
A lie? But you a flawless mirror glass?

# The Standard Egg

The standard egg behaved as it should not;
When Mother looked she saw a monster grown,
A cackler with no fangs, a horny snout,
A featherbed on legs with flapping skin.
For one not learned in the chromosomes,
It must have been a shock to see this young
Absurdity step forth and join his kin,
And seek to coil, who was not trim and long
But plump and buoyant, built for trees not slime.

Alas Charles Darwin did not know the id,
His famous *Origins* are only half of it.
The other half has been outlined by Freud,
And so we know how tragic was that bird.
Think of his childhood, born a sport among
A reptile brood and seeking to belong.
All others silent, he alone could sing,
All others crawlers, he alone could fly,
And yet he only practiced in the night,
His trauma, inability to glide
Down fallen tree trunks as his brothers did.

Heroic mutant, now analysis
Can recreate your adolescent stress.

28

It was castration fears that made you leap
Beyond your brothers, fearful for your wings.
Had no neurotic tensions worked their strain,
You might have made adjustment as a snake.
We would be birdless, without coop or hen,
No turkey in the freezer, no eggs with ham,
No feather mattresses, no Audubons,
No swans to rape our girls, get heroes born.
Conflicted rebel, rising in the dawn,
We might be snakes ourselves had you conformed.

## Miss Susie Beddoes

On a moon-white meadow
In another world,
I saw Miss Susie Beddoes,
In a smock of gold,
Walking with the nine
Holy Sisters she adores
From her roof-top studio
Where she paints from nine to four.
In that moon-white meadow,
Frozen with great stars,
They who had never
Visited her before,
Opened sacred eyes,
And it was their light
She wore.
It was their silk
In which she danced;
Her spinster limbs
Whirled with their voices,
Raising hymns
Of praise to all the
Talentless who sing
In those cold wastes of longing—
Which are her end.

30

Faster and faster I saw
Miss Beddoes turn
Until she was the meadow
And the antic flame,
The silver that the fickle
Sisters danced upon,
The martyred ghosts
From which their spirits sprang.

# At the River's Edge

Into the garden Nebuchadnezzar, wild stallion,
Neighing with the wind, where the peacocks
Run in hasty flight from your stamping hooves;
Over your shoulders the torn purple and on
Your head agog the golden crown; into the garden
From the tables where the weeping queen bunches
Her children into her arms. Oh divinity's askew,
Wild horse-god, trampling down the flower beds,
Crawling on earth, hair into dirt, eating the buds.

Your chieftains come, whispering, gesticulating,
Shadows on the Euphrates. Your concubines strut
White-legged through the glazed-brick rooms.
High on the ziggurats, astrologers foretell
Division of your kingdom and murder of your heirs.
But you, forgetful of your sceptered
Strength, graze in the twilight at the river's edge.

# Flight of the Children

From Corbeyville to Mount Laison
The train pursued an upward grade.
Like clustered grapes, the children sat
Within the coaches, undismayed.

From Mount Laison to Bar La Manche
The mountains rushed to level plains.
The children saw the steady black
Destroyed by red and yellow stains.

At Bar La Manche they found the sea
And sunrise on the eastern tip
Disclosed the agony of death
In sinking of a merchant ship.

The sunset of the second day
The flaming planes came overhead,
And played cantatas in the sky
With throated instruments of lead.

The wail of children in the train
Evoked antiphonal sound of shells,
And bursts of white against the red
Gardened the sky with asphodels.

At length they came to Gare du Coeur
To where the dignitaries stood;
But though they moved on live-white legs,
Their minds had turned to steel and wood.

# The Sea! The Tide!

At Larchmont the summer brought the white geese boats
Sauntering with supple walk the mermen's teeth.
We watched the point of sails the leader wore,
Masterson's boat, to where it danced the line.

Why then, we wondered, should the tall man seek
Divinity in making halliards wail; God's hand
Upon the tiller when in streets it was the devil's
Splay foot that he walked.

                      Abomination of the chairs,
With laurel head and whiskey breath, the ship,
Her cradle arms about his thighs, into the yellow
Cataracts of evening,
                    There goes Masterson!
                    The Sea! The Tide!

# Episode

You have returned from Rutland Fair
With roses in your hair
And skeletons in your eyes.
You have returned with cankers in your mind
And wire in your sighs.

You will not smile nor understand the tom's meow,
Nor rise to pick the apples from the bough.
You sit and grasp the silver spoon and pewter dish;
I serve you wine and meat and roasted fish.

# The Sea Horse

We often walked the sea wall in a storm;
My mother's arm stretched out to where the sea horse
    ran.
Hear him, she'd say, he's pawing at the surf.
If thunder came I'd think it was his neigh.

At home it was the études that she'd play;
Her prisoner eyes were soft as were the notes she struck.
But when the sea horse ran the canyons, wet with spray,
They caught his strength and from their dungeons broke.

# The Sea Is Acquisitive

The sea is acquisitive, taking back
Seaweed, shells, driftwood,
Accepting those humans who care to jump
   From Orizabas.

Life is presumed to have come from it,
But it wears also this aspect of death,
And I am fearful for a man who loves
   The sea too much.

Lately I have felt this in myself
And I must come to terms with it.
I have been too much alone,
   Walking on beaches.

This is, perhaps, what the Greeks meant
When they warned against the Sirens;
But oh Ulysses lied—nothing keeps out
   Its fantastic singing.

# The Changeling

My father surely was a king,
My mother an empress in India.
I do not want these worn-out hands
Stroking my face. The room is strange.
Who has stolen me from my bed?

But that was years ago, was years!

Or, perhaps, it was a witch who changed
My mother into this old hag.
Wicked sorceress, return!
Where are the gardens and the serving maids?
Where has the king, my father, gone?

# Legions of My Mind

Legions of my mind destroyed the world;
I sent them forth on forays, brutal troops,
Burning and sacking villages and farms.
Only this one small country did I keep,
This fortress with the dark, surrounding hills,
This neuter sun, gray disk which never sets,
But like a great hawk circles on and on.
Here is it ever twilight, blurred and cold;
Sentinels tour the masonry and search
The compass points from which no raid appears.
Hostile adventurer—if one still lingers there—
No longer do I seek love, I ask your hate;
Come with your idiot steeds of strength,
And rescue me from the evil I have done.

# The Chamber of the Dead

The chamber lies beneath the ground.
The entrance opens to my touch.
The stairway leads me down and down,
And none may follow to that spot.

Upon the walls my sacred art
Has painted its religious scenes,
Its savior gods, its phallic rites,
Its resurrections from the grave.

And round and round as priest I go,
Reading the stations, weeping love,
But all the miracles are past,
And only paint and dream live on.

If only flame would burn it down!
If only wind would sweep it clean!
Why do I so protect this death
Which like a leopard feeds on me?

# The Gulls

The gulls are hunting
In the mist,
The fishing fleet
Is moving down the bay.
There is nothing in the world
But this,
Here in this world,
Nothing but the bay,
And the gulls
Diving through the mist,
And the fishing fleet
Off with the first of day.
There is nothing
Better or worse than this,
The water's motion,
And the gulls' drab gray;
Nor any stronger hope
Than this:
These black craft
Sailing on their way.

# Aegeus

And from the cape he saw
The mourning sails,
And he mourned in his heart the death of his veins,

And he mourned in his mind
The gallant eyes
Which stared at him from the depth of night.

Dark flotilla
Come from the south;
Slowly it entered the blue of the bay,

And it blunted even
The sharpness of rocks;
All lay black under its wings.

Theseus did you
Will him slain?
Did you covet his kingdom, lust for his queen?

Perhaps the monster
Returned with you,
Your flesh the labyrinth in which it dwelt.

# First World

And that first world incessantly reborn,
That primal, golden age of giant fronds,
That timeless time of soaring, vernal suns,
Near to us through our daughters and our sons,
Reminds us of our loss, how much is done,
We who have watched a golden age turn bronze.

The first fruit still is heavy on the bough,
The first bird singing in the fragrant dawn;
No leaf has withered, not one light beam gone;
Man still is innocent, his fall to come.

See, those immortals walking hand in hand!
Hear, that sweet laughter carried by the wind!
Listening, we can almost understand
The arcane language of repose again.

# In the Calm of Midnight

In the calm of midnight
Is holy ground.
In the groves of silence
A god is found,
Bone-white and old,
And we worship alone.
By the words of our prayers
Our crimes are known.
By the sacrifice given
We atone:
The murderer's knife,
The adulterer's lust,
On the altars of slumber
Burn to dust.
In the ritual dance
The day is unwound.

## Death Date of a God

As though it were the death date of a god,
The waves wore black and sea bells rang
In the surly surf; as though He were
Nailed to a cross or impaled on a limb,
The wind cried horror and the rain
Fell like the tears of a heavenly throng.

As though it were the doom date of the spring,
And all the potency of light was done,
And never again would sunlight rear
Out of the ocean, flower and frond,
Mammal and reptile, black rose from the waves,
Steamed from the sand, conquered the world.

As though it were the death date of a friend,
And all his pain had found my flesh,
And all his meaning turning meaningless,
It was my sorrows that the sea bells tolled,
It was my darkness that the storm clouds bred,
And I walked alone through a world of death.

As though it were the doom date of my flesh,
Black threatened me, night sought my ruin.

46

# Porphyry's Journey

*in memory of Norma Sager*

It is not enough that the spring returns,
That lilac and daffodil again
Rise from the nothingness of death,
Last year's purple is not upon the bush,
The yellow that delights me only counterfeits
A yellow that is lost. My mind reflects
Lost seasons and lost hours, is not content
With what is similar, would have them back
Pure as the essence it has refined
Out of the tumult of insistent fact. And so
I greet the spring with music not in tune
Completely with the frolic of fresh buds;
I cannot join the chorus of forgetful things,
Choiring bird, gamboling brute,
Praising as though this were the only spring.
My mind becomes a voyager;
I seek a spring beyond the spring.

Cut in the brickworks of his heart,
Porphyry found a hidden stairs,
Mounted past globes and revolving skies
To reach the secret keystone of the world
And May was there, unblemished green,
And song was there, such melody

That bathing in that vernal stream
The filth of time fell from his brain;
The ancient rage that pain and joy had wrought
Was calmed; and, younger than the youngest thing,
He felt his roots take root in spring.
Who would not root himself in such a soil,
In such a climate put out leaves?

# The Prodigals

How does one pass from gray, returning find
A red and amber world of noon again?
There it was once, easy to be had,
Not loved and understood enough, too commonplace
To win devotion of the filial blood;
Too gracious in its openness, too kind
With all its vivid courtesies to keep at home
Prodigals who heard through drifting mist
The boiling music of the sun.
But the course of Phaëthon soon is run,
And Icarus drops from aerial realms
To zero emptiness. Stranded on the moon,
I watch the stars parade from east to west,
And try to recollect how flesh turns flame.

# The Reckoning

Number the loves that you have known,
Now gone.
Reckon the eyes that once could change
A universe of stone
Into a cosmos of green and red,
All fled.
Think of the beliefs that could estrange
You from your own.
What have they bred?
They were not worth the loss of one!
This do they own,
Gray with its dread.

# Lord in My Heart

My will cannot destroy this one
Who meditates above its flames;
He's stronger than its loves and hates.
Beyond the surge and shock of time,
He questions sun and moon and sky,
Leafs through the years, cuts into light.

He does not mind that all reply
Equivocations; still he works
Unravelling adjectives and nouns
To capture seasons at their birth,
The thunder of the primal green
As it bursts forth in bud and leaf.

My will cannot corrupt his will
Whose will is truth; lord in my heart,
Desire does not bring him down
To common roads that lead to hope.

Alas, I find my world in ruins
Because of him and yet I must
Still bend the knee and kiss the hand
That levels all my vanity

And makes me outcast in a void
Of shifting shadows, vacant winds.
When will my will accept his reign?

# Seas and Seasons

I

Seas and seasons, bird calls in the dawn,
Blooms and blossoms, drifting leaves
Showering down upon the stone
Of city streets, the sound of rain,
And spangled gowns my mother wore,
And red clown-faces three tiers down,
Grinning through hoops while women flung
Themselves through space; vision and dream,
Perfume and poison, rapture and pain,
Float through my mornings, haunt my dawns,
Rise in my evenings, a winter wind
Rattling the windows, a crimson sun
Dying in cloud-banks, enough to begin
Passage of seas and seasons again.

II

And the waters move, and the swimmers dive
Into great breakers, and the children play
At the edge of the surf, and then it is time
To pack one's belongings and walk from the beach
As the falling twilight cools the streets,
As heat-lightning flashes across the bay,
As blinds are drawn and it is good night,
And it is good morning and the beach again.

So many beaches! At Larchmont there were
White prows against green, gold pennants and spray,
And we shouted with joy as the racers flew
Over the surface of the summer sea.
And at Biarritz, anchored beyond the rocks,
Were pleasure cruisers, and I read their names
Lettered in black upon their hulls,
And I noted the ports from which they came.
And we motored to Nice and the water was warm,
The beach was stony and we did not stay.

So many vistas of ocean and sand,
Palm trees and jetties, sandpipers and terns,
So many place-names beaten from foam—
The years are ocean ruffled by wind;
And the tides rush in and the tides retreat,
And the new moons rise and the old moons thin.

III
Always there came those days when storm
Angered the waters, when a downpour of rain
Beat on the roofs and the sea birds screamed
Desolate songs as they hunted in gray;
And sometimes that meant the summer's end,

54

And hustle and bustle and stations and trains.
Journeys were once a frolic of fields,
A whirl of forests, a vision of towns,
A legend of trestles and mysterious curves,
And I sat at the window delighted by barns,
By windmills, by herds of horses and cows,
Feeding in silence on the slopes of soft hills.

And homecomings once were opening the door
To summer chintzes and raising the blinds
In parlor and study and viewing again
The curio case with its creatures of jade,
Its creatures of ivory, sequestered and calm:
Imperious cats and men from strange lands.
Autumn was once a return to one's own,
Mirrors that knew you and newels that recalled
The touch of your fingers going upstairs.

IV
I have lost a world of brownstones and staid
Elders moving through exalted rooms.
I have watched a youthful cosmos decay,
Years and decades undermine
The roots of shade trees. I have seen their limbs

Fall from sick sockets. I have stood at graves
And felt the vigor of life descend
To a bloodless region of memory and pain.

The seasons still swing with the drift of the stars,
The tides still obey the sway of the moon,
The wheel of light and dark revolves,
But I have seen into the heart of things.
I know the fierceness of the diving bird,
The lust of leaves, the treachery of waves,
The arrogance of stone, the scorn of rain,
And knowing these things I cannot praise
As I praised once, not knowing that I praised.

v
O I shall not praise again! I shall not sing
The merit of warm purple nor the eyes of dawn.
I shall not rise in youth to honor youth,
The time of simple love and faith is gone.
I cannot beg it back from windy nights,
Nor steal it from the violent young;
The wonder's locked within their flesh,
Fed by the fires of their blood.

I shall not swim again in gentle seas,
Nor climb grave mountains into clouds,
Trusting the kindness of their slopes,
Unmindful of their sharp ravines;
Nor can I even wish to praise,
Nor do I have the heart to sing,
Once more a child with childish thoughts,
Tied to the whirl of wind and rain.

VI

And seas and seasons come to wound,
And blooms and blossoms open graves,
And newels speak of vanished halls,
And trestles tell of long-dead days.
So many blossoms, so many buds,
So many dawn-birds singing in gray,
Singing in green, so many suns
Rising and setting, the way I have come
Is a golden tempest, the days of my pain
Are a rush of music dying away.

O voices gathered! O visions known!
You have fed on my flesh and drunk of my blood.
O incontestable wonders! you have shaped my veins

57

From your riot of passion. You have sharpened my eyes,
And now I am not content with the turn
Of summer to winter, of winter to spring,
Of day into night and joy into pain.
O once belovèd! my love would find
Water-worlds beyond the tides,
Sweeter fragrances than country nights
—How can I speak but from what I know?
How can I dream but in touch and sight?—
But not those fragrances that quickly go,
And not those waves that surge and beat:
Fragrance without the dying rose,
Water without the nervous seas.
Is there such perfume? Are there such floods?
Do you, my dead, enjoy such calm,
Freed from your loves, freed from your hates,
At last that beauty you sought to become?

# The Tyrants

Some worlds are best left buried, not brought forth
To tyrannize again the liberated blood.
Some deaths are violence not to be undone;
When ghosts walk, let them lie below
The stone and rubble that bore down their flesh.
May no midnight stroke return them strength,
No heartfelt spell frame from the night
Casing of ligament and bone to bring
Them treading down the hallways of the dark,
Sceptered once more, clad in imperial silk,
Requiring their ancient privileges and rights;
Neither the Byzantine hierarchs, pontiffs of time,
Who ruled over childhood, nor the sequestered queens,
Island personages in whose service one's youth
Was spent on fraudulent Odysseys,
Nor the lesser princes of dissident realms
For whose dogmas one suffered disgrace and hate.
Some thrones are best left vacant,
Some deserted halls never unboarded.
Though one's spirit thirsts, hating unbounded
Freedom, some faiths should be lost.

# Once

Once if a doom-wind shrilly cried,
A witch in the evening haunting my room,
Or the terrible shadows massed on the walls,
Talons extended, saber teeth bared;
Once if the black night pressed too hard
Against my closed lids and I screamed for fear,
Feeling the menace of death and change,
Though I could not have told what I feared;
The opening door would let in light,
And monsters and shadows would flee as they heard
A soft voice of comfort and witches would reel
Knowing they could not resist the strength
Of the warm-eyed protectress who kept me safe,
Of the brown-haired Titan who ruled the dawn,
Directed the daylight, shuffled the months,
Whom mirrors honored and shade trees adored.
Oh once if the hanging moon hung awry,
If the splashing waves did not break as they should,
If the sun was hidden or the storm-clouds blurred
The flanks of the hills, it was to her I prayed,
And I watched the magic of her potent smile
Alter the weather, reverse the tides;
I saw the industry of her learned hands
Order the madness and maelstrom of time.

# Ascent from the Dead
*for Elaine Gottlieb*


But shall I mourn forever an old world lost?
Shall I enervate seasons by dead hues
Not clearly recalled? Shall I ask of green
That it be the sweet singer of my first springs
Or nothing? Shall I permit my eyes
To subvert the harmonies of soaring birds,
And read their dissidence into forest lakes
And mountain vistas? In fine shall I die
Because a certain order has passed from earth?

If youth were everything, succeeding times
Merely the corruption of original joy,
Midway would mark the extent of life,
For who would stay to see the thrusting years
Impertinently work upon his flesh?
Yet from their sick beds the agèd call
For light, more light, and die demanding dawn.
Clearly such death's-heads are insane or else
They come on motives unknown to the young.

And sometimes on an evening I can find
Meaning enough within a graying sky,
Reason enough in fragrance of June vines
To keep one's veins eternally alive,

One's senses always seeking out rapport
With all the teeming loveliness of time.
Sometimes, advancing on a summer beach,
All questions fade within the drifting foam,
And, won by amethyst, I am at peace.

Peace, then, is possible; joy can survive
The advent of wisdom, the fractured dream
Of a garden world in which sun and stars
Were jubilant servants contriving change.
Rapture is possible though the wind
Is unmasked and viewed on its selfish wings,
An impartial destroyer driving through space.
Meaning is possible though dissension rends
The magnificent members of dark and light.

# FROM *Porphyry's Journey*

## Last Love

After all loves have failed, it's love that leads
The failing spirit down to death:
It's deep-sea reveries of drifting doves
Knelling the oblivion of possible flesh:
It's screens of dreaming, driving light
From objects that might pierce through pain,
And urge the outward arms to clasp
More than a mist that haunts the mind.

After all deaths have died, it's night that comes
Bejeweled and masked, its peacock gown
A ripple, ruffle, of all bays and hills,
All lips, hands, eyes, that bind the brain
To joy, past joy. Last love must hide
Its jet-black bosom and its formless face.

# Seascape

A seascape turned bird on a gray-blue day,
Soared toward the sun, and Orpheus, dead,
Rose from the limepit, threw off the stone,
Awakened by wings of seaweed and spume.
He called to his bride and Eurydice came,
Shaping from moss and pebble and slime.

A flower turned lion, ranged through the skies,
Rumpled the firmament, snapped at the stars,
And, deep in the earth, Elijah stirred,
Fractured the roots which grew from his heart;
And his fingers broke through the crust of earth,
And he bled the grass and sprang forth a youth.

A tune drifted down through a rent in the sky,
And walked on the hills and scattered wild seed,
And the hills changed into glistening wheat,
And the wheat changed into a marching throng,

Shouting Hosannah and Christ is our king,
We are risen from death, Tammuz we hymn.
A sun became granite, and a seascape returned;
A gray-blue day advanced to its end.
A lion turned flower and Orpheus died;

Elijah lay down in his grave again;
And a needle of lightning mended the sky,
And the music changed to thunder and wind.

# The Islands

Say to the islands I shall not return!
And where are the islands? Are they still bound
In the hair of the mermaid, two white palms,
The hands of love, ambitious and strong?
Say to the islands my faith is gone,
My belief in their warmth, the sweep of their winds;
This colder climate has chilled my bones,
And I live so old and changed and done,
What are the voyages of my youth but lies,
Or the tales of another a century dead?
The generations spin other forms
Who win those coasts and adore those woods.
Let them go raving on and on,
Searches that failed, passions I had.

# On the Death of an Old Man

Yield of a lifetime is what yield?
What treasures gathered are shadowy woods
And evanescent faces and subtle silks
Torn from their roots in the world of fact,
Spirited into silence to be ceaseless flow
Among restless turnings of parks and lakes,
And swans' eyes burning with loves and hates,
Imbued with desires they never know?
O the cloak is falling from this agèd heart,
The streams are flowing back to death,
The garnered clouds, the hoarded hills and skies,
Released from sorrow, from their whirling stress,
Drift to the dark where their substance has gone.
And the tired wrinkles smooth in the gray
Of early twilight, and the hands untwine!

# Halfway

Halfway across this riot and this song,
This carnal bloom and blemish, I become
Dooms I have seen and cities I have worn,
Faiths I have nurtured, betrayals undergone;
Learn that the figure, when the figure's done,
Will not be that fine image, boasting tongue
In tavern youth sang forth, encomium
Praising itself, itself, not one third known.

Halfway across this fury and this foam,
Meeting myself in hall or drawing room,
Coming upon myself in garden scene,
I blame the age, contentious, evil times,
I blame the indecisions of my mind;
I mourn the promise that so soon has flown.

# My Nursemaids Sang a Tapestry

My nursemaids sang a tapestry;
I cut the cloth and stitched the hem.
Joseph's coat of many hues
Was scarcely lovelier than mine.

I had the geese flock in its wild
Endeavor south upon my heart.
A dreaming lady on a hill
Smiled sleepily up at the stars.

And all the flowers of the world
Were woven in a rich brocade.
Beauty was everywhere I went
Since in such gardens I was robed.

First it was rain that streaked the dyes;
Then fire embossed a cicatrice
Upon the dreaming lady's face,
And vultures flew where had been geese.

Destruction of the arbors brought
Whirlwind of petals, earth and stone;
And naked trellises raised arms
To blind the stars and leech the sun.

## An Oriole

This poem springs from a moment which was not grasped,
When chill in the garden, feeling the damp twilight,
And smoking a cigarette, I saw an oriole

Which suddenly rose from the bush to the telegraph
Wires—remembering it is beyond the literal flash
Of the obscure darks and golds which were never sure,

Erasing these present moments of men in a room,
Talking across typewriters, large in their occupation
Of space, sprawling and dissident, until perhaps

They too will become poems which the mind can
Digest, after its fashion, cutting away the extraneous,
And knowing them where they no longer exist.

## The Persians

Who are these Persians moving among
The scurrilous parakeets?
You fellows, I remember you;
You are the conscripts who fled
And did not fight at the passes.
For five years you have been here
Among the parrots, and Darius is dead;
A long five years of queens
Made concubines and concubines made queens.
Persia is sick but you are laughing,
And the winging birds are laughing.
"Darius is dead," they repeat
As if it were a singing.
"Persia is sick," and go on turning.

# On the Death of a Carp

Now drift and flail, and this is death,
The silver body manacled to pain.
O swift, sweet song, impassioned rage
Of moonlight weaving round and round,
Changed and so changed, yes this is death;
This is what moonlight must become,
Fiercely turned poison, stoked to flame,
Wasting the tissue on which it leans.

The others still are musical and sound,
Dash through the greenery their fluted tones,
Warble the waters in octaves of praise,
Thrill the warm surface with their radiant forms.
No mourning for him so suddenly gone;
Here, and forever, their frolic maintains.

# Flute Song

Thirteen times the clanking flute song
Of Monsieur Varoni rang.
The white-shirted audience applauded,
And particularly the blond-haired girl
Varoni kept.
Thirteen performances breathing forth
His thought in meticulous cacophonies!
(A discreet passion, the critics wrote;
Varoni shows style and bitter understanding.)
The blond-haired woman didn't know.
Perhaps an astute biographer, questioning her,
Through her, could have penetrated
To the soul of Varoni,
The mind and body of him assuming
Grotesqueries of attitudes and understanding.
Perhaps he could have anticipated
The fourteenth performance
Which came out no longer bitter and hard,
But soft and sentimental, self-pitying,
Gushing with the mawkish ego
Of Monsieur Varoni.

# By Ancient Calendars Undone

By ancient calendars undone,
By flesh that walked before my flesh,
By battles waged in fallen lands,
Dream of my veins you have been spun
By waters I have never seen;
Guilt of my tongue, my speech was said
A thousand centuries by vicious winds.
Out of the wilderness, cur and cat;
Out of the skies, a plunging bird:
All of the blood upon its beak,
All of the passion of its wings.
By ancient calendars adorned,
By colors clasped to dying eyes,
By grace of savage and of priest,
Lobes that acquired thought and song,
Treading the moment of my time,
Leading the moment on and on
To future calendars beyond
The interest of my hands and bone.
By future calendars I shall be known,
Anonymous though my acts become.

# Lorenzo's Invocation

Lights, bring me lights! This darkness hems me round,
Sleep rising from a sea of endless sleep.
Let singers stir me from this emptiness
With bawdy words reminding me of nights
I walked disguised along the city streets
Myself a minstrel praising precious love,
And there were youthful lips to bite and kiss.
Push back the shadows, let me breathe again,
And I will fall to death through loveliness,
Shimmering images of distant springs.
Now in the gloom they mount and one by one
I meet the perfumed faces of the past,
Hands that were laid to rest unclench from bone,
Adore and caress and voluptuous eyes,
Long since acquainted with the sting of dust,
Forget the lessons of the frigid grave.
Then let it come, now death be kind and swift
Before the crypts release unwanted ones;
If death is darkness in that night escape
Is certain; they will never find me out.
I win release. Why do I mourn at death?
It is my sanctuary, my great hope,

The iron doors I lock against my foes
Living and dead. Within the vault of earth
I find my innocence and peace once more.

# A Visitor at Breakfast

An organization of the flesh,
Gold and white, and ribald red,
Fantastic as a Hindu queen,
Partakes of breakfast in her bed.

An organization of the mind
Accounts for laughter and the shrill
Monopoly of verbal sounds
Which billow to the windowsill.

The courtiers, who with servile steps,
Are Tom and Sue, the serving maid,
Are organized to find in her
The beauty of the proud obeyed.

But I who come, the visitor
Intruding into Fragonard,
Have on my clothes the odor of
The stone and brick within the yard.

And stone and brick, perhaps, are why
I feel a darkness in this room,
And know her as the Queen of Death
Who weaves our sadness on her loom.

# In the Castle Crypt

He who pursued the Moors
In holy wars
Waits.

Captain who bore
Christ's standard
To the gates

Of infidel cities,
He stands sculpted
At the portcullis of night.

Recognize him, Heaven,
If he still sleeps
In this granite crypt,

If your moat bridge down
Has not known
His warlike step.

See, his visor is up!
And you can read
His ancient grief:

Jerusalem untaken,
And the armies
Breaking faith.

Why do you torment me,
Old silence,
With your marble dreams,

When the spring is outside,
And the resurrection
Of the leaves?

# Steeplejack

What prayers I knew, what ladders to His heart;
In childhood I could wrench the years apart
(so few as yet) and, steeplejack of night,
Climb past cathedrals, till I drank the light
Of infant stars. At the birthplace of time
Throwing aside my body, I could be His mind.

I could touch the moon-embroidered robes of Him,
And speak the wordless language of cherubim.
Sacrilege was not, nor heresy, nor doubt;
I needed not instructions to find Him out.
My acrobatic flesh and spirit soared
Beyond the war of things to reach my Lord.

# The Arnold Arboretum

Bright, bright, bright
Are the gardens today;
Firebuds have been lit in the green
And the light
Is a living red
Though the skies are gray.
Each bush is burning;
Here are flaming trees
To heal the mind
If it would dare to be
sight, sight;
Its burning does not bring it ease;
Its blossoms are corollas
of the night,
Dubious blooms grown
From its own disease.
This is a burning
In which the heart must freeze,
And yet the will
Assents to its decay.
There is your God;
He lives within the day!
He burns, azalea brazier
of delight.

The bush will speak
If you approach its might,
Ecstatic fire flesh
Your corrupting clay.

# Jason

Where day and night meet
In the gardens of the east,
Hangs the fleece.
And were it merely gold,
I should not risk my youth
In such extravagant search.
And were it only symbol,
It would not be worth the loss
Of those who die
On the improbable islands
Mariners have reached
At the boundaries of sleep.
It is not the tunic of a god,
I think.
Where I sail god and man
Must struggle equally
To snatch a meaning
From the arcane tree
On the slope of time,
At the edge of hope,
Where the shuttling sun
Weaving mist,
Leaps from the aureate fleece.

# The Conflagration

Things cry their names
And perish in their names for me.
Perhaps they hide themselves in shame,
Perplexed by my perplexity.
I know the names of too many things.

If there was ever salutation
Leading beyond the names to flame,
That time is past.
The mind is fire burning what has been,
And what remains are charred and charring cognomens.

Oh creature world, come in, come in,
And be not ash but fire like my own,
Unnamed, unnameable and alone.
Fire mingling with fire might burn on and on,
And from the conflagration God be born.

# Descent of the Hero

Repeat your name when circling down
The silence of the onyx stairs.
Let memory trail you to the ground,
A string you wind and still unwind
As hell's gate opens to your tears.

Nowhere is vaster than the world;
Souls drift through nothing and they wear
The mimic shapes of what they meet.
You may become the face you seek;
She may put on your husk of care.

Out of yourself among the lost,
You do not know what lusts will chain,
You may stay on king of the dead,
Or sprout with flowers in the spring,
Or come alive in a dreamer's brain.

# The Fate of Rivers

A final drying up is the fate of rivers;
Beyond our eyesight the electrons flash.
Yahweh was god of the lightning and thunder;
Eden and Adam lie in volcanic ash.

Now there are no more Bibles to plunder.
What we do best is experiment with mass,
Shoot young men toward Mars and the Dipper,
Prevent crackups at the underpass.

Who will deny there was a certain elation
In rolling with darlings upon the grass,
In getting good grades and having ambition,
How could we know that we had turned to brass?

All that we had was a tentative equation,
Physicists studying Andromeda's gas,
Further findings and extrapolations,
There is no more time; our lives are past.

We have been stranded at some way station
In a draughty universe of spin and blast,

Lacking the spirit and concentration
To find ourselves and our lives are past.

All that we got was a tentative equation,
The movements of ions and the speeds of gas.

# Shadows

I can view them as heroes and let them be
All chthonic persons descending to the sea,
All lovers who have known death intimately.
But now as I grow older I prefer
Merely to watch the errant shadows stir.

How magnificent on a windy, driven noon,
Cut from their bodies and the wind's tune,
Dancing discovery, ecstatic, alone;
If I close my eyes shadows of tree and post
Whirl in my silence, tug at my ghost.

# The Fault

Do you recall how that year in the spring
We had no time for any visiting?
Death distant, yet so very near to us,
Seemed interruption and a foolish fuss.

A foolish fuss to mask our love in black,
And pray for one who could not journey back.
Our hard lust held us and we fled through rain,
Anxious to tangle and caress again.

How little value was the fault! I found
Within your shallow hardness my youth's wound.
Your stone scraped stone and there was blood beneath;
It was your flint that brought me down to death.

You do recall. Your eyes are not of stone,
And now turned flesh, you also must atone.

## August Storm

Here is that old god come again
Out of the east,
That jealous god of storm and lightning,
Scattering the fleet
Of trawlers busy in the gray,
Yahweh, dressed as whirlwind,
Kicking up the sea.
Despite certificates of death,
Filed in the nearby church,
Here is the old malice,
The ancient spite.
There will be leveling of our sea walls,
Disfigurement of earth.
Ah now the gulls scream
As though they willed
This show of might.
Wind! Wind! Rain! Rain!
No blue madonna will calm this surf.

# Fireworks

Plunging through the calm
Breath of his being,
Twisting irises of blue
Above the sea,
A god performs.
We think it is our guile.
Children clap hands and smile,
Seeing him twirl
Lariats of silver,
And juggle diamond ropes
At the peak of night,
A mountebank whose style
Is blast and spangle.
He holds the moon
Upon his hand
And breathes the frosty
Stars behind his game,
Illusionist,
Playing his scherzo
Of shaking lights
And shivering flames,
As though it were
The soul of him.

# Little Elegy

She who betrayed me is dead now,
And her children mourn
It must be so.
But it was not her crime to me
Which brought her low
Into the ground.
What her guilt was I do not know,
Other than that she was only flesh.
She should have been born
The image of my wish,
A shadow drifting in the snow
I dreamed long ago,
And I would have kept her
Safe from death
In the dim unreality flickering
Below breath.
But no, she had to be real
And walk upon the earth;
And the tears wept for her
Are real tears,
And the years of her ageing
Are my loss.

# River Views

1.

Blue as it was,
As it is on certain days
When the sky spills
Turquoise into its
Gray,
As it shall be again
When the wharves decay,
It is a water tiara
I hold before my eyes,
As though I had passed
Beyond the skies
Into Heaven's mind.
Do I enter?
Is it there I find
The imagination of blue
More true
Than the slippery, dun river
At evening,
Pouring its desolation
Into the bay?

2.

I know too well the deception of your wild wings
And your demented cries,

Magnificent birds of prey, circling in the mind.
A crimson waterfall spilled from the skies,
And I fell with it
Into those indigo pools you inhabit
And which I thought I had left behind.
Here by the river at sunset,
There are so many rivers to follow,
So many hues, passing from plausible gray
To improbable yellow,
My tumbling down into the fens
Where your maddened eyes
Burn like enchanted gems,
Was an enchantment chaining me to your pain,
Your restless turnings, the diving talons of you,
Driven worldward
By the concupiscence in your veins.

# Orpheus

I must find her;
Here in some meadow of myself
The song of an imaginary bird
May be her speech,
Or a flower growing in the shade
Of a thought
May have roots that reach
Through the ambiguous shadows
Into the night.
It is my destiny to fracture time,
And climb
To silence through the breach,
To touch a memory
And with a word
Kiss it awake.
I sing, and as the music
Glistens,
Others see her shape.
I listen but I know
The face is only mist.
The chord I need
Is hidden in my grief.

# The Gentle Women

With their mysterious clatter and their pale robes,
Seeing the sunset spatter and the garden flowers
That fold, and at the gate, coming up in their gray
Tweeds, their men from the trains as sure as the

Evening; with the children's laugh and the dog's ears
Bending, catching a distant sound, and their world
Fragile as china, chintz, the lace in their curtains;
Dreaming of fountains evoked by hands hitting the

Sevenths, and knowing tragedy as the woman who dies
In the eighteenth chapter; with blood a remembrance
Of the time their fingers were pricked and the fall
Of the nations distant across the sea where the armies

Have been; when the houses crumble and the street men
Whirl, rioting the dark cities and the Caesars ride,
Then will the gentle women rise from their chairs
And walk into the silence where Antoinette sleeps.

# The Betrayal

I do not remember that childhood world of centaurs,
Though sometimes waking at night I hear the hooves
Of the lascivious herds cantering into the forest,
And I can almost taste a ritual of forbidden flowers
Among moon-maidens, pink as the flesh of morning.
My first recollections are of innocence.
A pantheon had fallen, yet I knew not of betrayal.
Shrines had been deserted and worshippers left sighing
For the impassioned spirits banished to silence.
My guilt! My guilt! I sometimes dream the violence,
The final frolic after the bribe had been taken,
When I with secret knife approached the altar,
And plunged it deep into the green god's heart.

# Calm, Suave and Blue

Calm, suave and blue our mother lies;
Our mistress breathes with drifting waves.
Today the Virgin kisses rocks,
And on her bosom bears the gray
Of friendly gulls.

            They nurse and play
As though these great limbs were forever kind,
As though this kirtle blue, this wimpled face,
Could not accept the mood of winds.

O mother, on those screaming autumn days
When the reefs cry from the lash of pain,
Then, then, we know wherefore is our sin,
From whom we have learned our malice,
            Why we betray.

# The Lines on the Dunes

Here is a wind-net woven out of wire,
The dune blasts shake on stormy, autumn evenings,
And the summer birds use as a perch for preening.
How white this mesh when touched by winter fire . . .
Its mile on mile gleams in the noontide burning.
Its shadow changes with the daylight's turning,
And at night it is nowhere unless the moon
Plays it as though it were a giant lyre,
But when silver fingers strike, it sounds no tone;
And yet its cables ring with man's desire.
Through its silk one sees the wild clouds running,
Those ancient warriors who will bring it down.

# In the Garden

As one who mourns the lost untruth of youth,
       She moves in her garden,
Tending the spring flowers that are her hours.
       She will not pardon
The seasons of marigolds that have destroyed
       Her powers.
       Trivial! Trivial!
Time dissipates and sours.

What for her the stir of new leaves,
       Believing as they come?
She knows their showy adolescence will succumb
       To the cruel abrasion of the air.
The best is always first, and then comes thirst,
       And the pain of care.

Prune! Prune! Use the shears.
She is that death she has rehearsed in dream,
       And yet she wears
Shuddering carmen at her breast,
A ravished rose that dances with her breath.
       Rose, rose window
       Looking out beyond the world!
But she has never gazed into its depth.

# *Prose*

\* \* \* \*

# At the End of Summer

"You're sure you don't want to go, Vivian?"

"I'm tired, Larry. If you want, go without me."

"Not even for a few minutes?"

"Honestly not, Larry."

They stood on the dock of their property, looking out into darkness. It was the end of summer; night had come quickly. Some of the cottagers had already departed and there were not so many lights fringing the lake as at the beginning of the season; in mid-July there had been a brilliant cluster every fifty feet, and the shoreline sparkled after sundown. But though that dazzle had passed, the crickets still sang. Vivian heard a vivacious chorus exulting in the woods and fields behind her. She was also conscious of the monotonous ripple of the water.

Larry touched her arm. "It's just that you're tired, honey? Nothing more?"

She laughed. "Oh, Larry, you're always conjuring up phantoms."

"Shall I get your coat?"

"No, I'm not cold."

She wished that he would let her be. All day, sensing that there was something wrong, he had been after her. It was his intuitive nature, almost more female than hers. The only way to avoid his interrogations was to go to Hebart's party, but she wondered if she could endure being in that man's presence. She took her husband's hand in hers. "Larry, I'm tired and nervous. That's all. Let me fret by myself."

He remained standing close to her, a protective shadow hovering in the dark. He was thirty-five, seven years older than she, and had been her teacher, having plucked her from a collection of handsome young women who had comprised a seminar in Romantic poetry. Since he had been a bachelor at a girl's college, something like that had been bound to happen.

There was a sudden flash of light across the cove and a rocket went up, spangled into a hundred blue lights. For a moment the face of the water was visible, dark and impenetrable. Vivian shivered.

"Isn't that just like Bill?" she said. "He treats his going away like the Fourth of July."

"What's happened between you two?" Larry asked.

"You haven't quarreled?"

"Nonsense, Larry. But you know he likes to show off."

"Vivian, you must get your coat. It's chilly. You're trembling."

Another rocket soared and then a third. Vivian, hearing laughter and a jumble of voices, imagined Hebart standing with his guests clustered around him, match in hand, igniting fireworks. He would be—as always—smiling superciliously.

"You're right, Larry," she said. "It is chilly. Let's go into the house."

She turned and he followed her. From across the cove came the sound of dance music. She was familiar with all those tunes, the dozen records that Hebart had found in the cottage. It had once been amusing to dance to them but now the music seemed garish and uninspired. Nor though she rattled pots and pans in the kitchen could she escape the noise of the celebration. Tomorrow night the lights in Hebart's cottage would be extinguished.

She walked back into the living room where Larry was reading the paper.

"Oh, let's go after all," she said. "I don't feel like making dinner."

"Sure," Larry agreed, "a few hours away from here will do wonders for you."

:

There was, she realized, a sort of bravado in her going. She was the rejected woman and was not expected to show up despite the invitation. But now that she had altered her decision, her flair for the dramatic took over. Larry exclaimed when he saw her slip into a green gown that was rather too fancy for the occasion.

"Good God, Vivian, what's that? This isn't a formal dinner." He was putting on a sport shirt and Bermuda shorts.

"Oh I just want to, Larry. Who knows when I'll get dressed up again?"

She was aware that her attitude had once more awakened his anxiety. But he didn't suspect, nor would he ever. Hebart was right about him. He was a typical American, a "do-gooder" who had had no real contact with the universe. His Ph.D. had given him only a worthless jargon—the dates of Keats' birth and death, when the Lyrical Ballads had been published. Hebart had shown her what she had suspected all along, that she was married to a mediocrity.

Standing in front of the dressing table, she put on earrings. She was thin, dark-haired and olive-complexioned. Larry had told her over and over again that she had a Botticelli face; it was a trifle too long in her opinion. But she had known since childhood that she was pretty enough.

He came up behind her and put his arms about her. "You look lovely," he said. Her body tensed. He kissed her on the neck. "There's nothing to worry about."

"I told you, Larry, that I'm not worried."

She wondered what he would do if she turned and confessed that she was an adultress, and that the child she was carrying might not be his. His greatest moment of irritation, it seemed to her, had been when he had not received his associate professorship the year he thought he should have. For two nights he had railed about the duplicity of the English department. What had happened now was surely a greater duplicity than that. She watched his goings and comings in the mirror, observing the slight pout on his face which was there she guessed because he sensed he was excluded from her confidence. The world was a dark and terrible place and Larry walked through it as if he were involved in an innocent game. Half his life was over, his head was balding, and he remained an adolescent. Say what you would about Hebart, he was at least a man. And she was a woman. These five months had proved that all too conclusively. The fireworks were still going on and she moved to the window.

"Ready?" Larry asked.

"Yes," she answered.

As she walked onto the porch, she thought she felt life moving within her, but she knew that it was impossible, the child not having yet reached that stage of development.

Larry wanted to go the long way, taking the road that wound around the lake, having become particularly protective since he had been informed of her pregnancy. Vivian insisted on using the path through the woods which in summer was scarcely discernible even during the day. The moon had disappeared behind some clouds, and moving into the pine grove, they found themselves in a solemn darkness. "Watch your step," Larry had warned. She was surprised how happy he had been when she had told him he was to be a father. Presumably he had wanted a child all along and had merely pretended he was uninterested because he realized motherhood had no appeal for her. He was foolish but generous. All these years he had tolerated her moods. Now she felt sorry for him, but while the affair had been in progress, she had been indifferent to the injury she was doing him. It would have been better, she realized, if they had never met. He had wanted a secure, placid existence writing his academic papers and gathering his anthologies. She had never brought him anything but trouble.

Her foot caught on the root of a tree and his arm supported her. Impulsively she pulled herself free, angry that his aid should have proved necessary.

"I'm not going to fall, Larry."

"How can you be sure, Vivian? You almost went right on your face."

She didn't care if she did fall, wished that some terrible accident would release the child from her womb. All her life she had brought people sorrow. She lengthened her stride and almost ran from the woods; Larry's footsteps followed her doggedly.

"Vivian, slow down."

"I can see where I'm going."

Always when she was in trouble she became drunk with emotion, as a child had had hysterical crying fits. Even the explanation of why she was behaving as she did became impossible for her. She remembered how on her sixteenth birthday she had cried all day looking ahead into the world and seeing only darkness. And here she was in that darkness, that terror that had both attracted and tormented her. As they walked through the dark woods, the memory of the last half year grew within her.

Snow had still been on the ground when they had arrived that March. There had been ice in the lake and they had been excited by the notion of being off in the woods with winter still around them. Larry intended to burrow in and get a hell of a lot of work done; he had the quarter off. "Isn't it a privilege," Vivian said, "to occasionally get away from people?" Her plan was to search the woods for the first violet. Larry told her that not even skunk cabbages would be around as yet.

It was on their second day there that they noticed a man walking near the lake. He appeared out of the pines, tall and massive, a veritable giant. The man wore an astrakhan overcoat and a fur hat; in one hand he carried a walking stick. Vivian and Larry had been going around in dungarees and lumberjackets, and smiled at each other, seeing such a dandy.

The man passed by without looking at them, but the next day strolled up to the porch and introduced himself. His name was Hebart, Bill Hebart, and he was renting the Cox's place. He'd been at the lake two weeks already and was happy to see other human faces. Vivian knew immediately from the joyous smile on Larry's lips that the stranger was someone important, but the name meant nothing to her. Later, after their guest had gone, she had been informed of his credentials. It was a stroke of luck, Larry said, to have him in the neighborhood. An aesthetician of the first rank wasn't available for discussion every day of the week. Hebart's articles on the Northern Renaissance and the decline of the classical in modern painting had to be considered definitive. And such a charming fellow.

Thereafter he had come often, and Larry's view of him had changed quickly. Hebart had always insisted that a bottle of Bourbon be in the house so he could drink himself sodden. On his way toward semi-unconsciousness, he passed through a series of stages beginning with a gentle maliciousness and ending up with outright insults. He liked to sit in the middle of the living room, obstructing the life of the house, and criticizing generally. No sooner did he discover that Larry was an authority on the Romantics, than he began an attack on Wordsworth. He couldn't understand how a mature man could have created such bathos. Vivian sought unsuccessfully to mediate that quarrel. After a while she gave up trying to be polite and let the men go on as furiously as they wished. "What do you get so upset for?" she kept saying to her husband. "He's obviously a hostile personality." At times the quarrels seemed to her totally irrelevant, as if Hebart were merely looking for an issue. It was obvious that he considered himself more intelligent and sensitive than the majority and had to make his point of view evident.

"All right, call me an aristocrat," he said. "What does that mean but the love of the best?"

For the last eighteen years he had been living in Europe and regarded himself as a European. Only occasionally did he return to his native country and then was repelled by it. "America should have stayed a forest," he said. "These woods are fine, but, Lord, the people!"

His very massiveness made his hatred more formidable. He was six feet seven of venom smiling contemptuously. Neither Larry nor Vivian was a chauvinist, but Hebart attacked with such acrimony that it was difficult not to be outraged. Americans were boors; they were badly educated; they were naive barbarians who were destroying the world. The only reason that Hebart was hanging around was that an aunt of his had died and he was waiting for the estate to get settled. He was to come into a little money which he needed badly. He had been born in Utica. He made a wry face. "That's really a city to escape from," he assured them.

Challenged to present his ideal, he offered the Greeks. "Of course, they're out of fashion," he laughed, "and so is beauty. Everything now has to be so expressive. The souls of serfs can only be stimulated by the crass. Look at America. It's nothing but a wilderness of phallic cities."

"Screw the Greeks," Larry said to Vivian one day. "We've go to cool this thing off. I can't stand much of that guy."

But that very evening Vivian heard something that changed her opinion of Hebart. Larry had driven down to town and Hebart and she sat in the living room drinking. For some time she and her husband had been speaking about Hebart's left eye which seemed to be lifeless. They wondered if it was glass. All of a sudden Hebart began speaking about the eye. "I suppose you've noticed my eye," he said. "It's glass, you know." He had been, he told her, in the Battle of the Bulge and was lucky to be alive. Fifteen pieces of shrapnel had been taken out of him.

"I regard everything that's going on now as a second life," he confessed. "Death doesn't disturb me; I've had it once."

—Lazarus, she thought. Yes, Lazarus—Hebart had been through the darkness and had returned. From that moment on his words acquired a new authority. But it continued to be difficult for her not to stare at the dead eye; it had become for her the central part of his body. Larry confessed that he had the same problem. "Poor son of a bitch," he said; "isn't it horrible?" But knowing that Hebart had been maimed gave, he thought, a clue to his psyche. Hebart, Larry supposed, held the nation responsible for his misfortune. Vivian regarded this explanation as superficial.

"No, I'm convinced that he sees more than we do."

"What does he see? He certainly talks a lot of nonsense."

"Oh, I don't mean about America. I mean about everything."

"That's some logic," Larry said, "One eye sees better than two."

But she was convinced, though she kept her thoughts to herself. The next time Hebart sat with them in the living room, drinking and arguing, he became his usual insulting self. But this time she thought: He's right. Why hadn't she recognized his insight in the first place?

Americans, he was saying were all too subjective, thought too much of their own feelings. Look at all the stuff the contemporary artists and writers spewed up. No wonder no one read fiction any more. The feeling for the work of art as a classic structure was gone. Everyone was too busy examining his guts. Surely there was something childish in all this subjectivity; Americans never grew up. What America needed was a cultural renaissance.

She was thinking: How true. In the circles she frequented everyone was concerned with his own subjectivity. Larry for example. He had sat out the war in a Replacement Training Center. She had long ago realized that his most sincere complaint about the hostilities was that his education had been interrupted. To Hebart she said, "What a wonderful thought. Do you really think some sort of renaissance is possible?"

Hebart said he didn't know.

Larry apparently didn't notice how often now the two of them were off in a corner talking softly. He was busy with his latest great project, a new anthology of Romantic poetry that he was preparing with a colleague of his named Williamson. After Memorial Day, he was often absent from the house, driving over the mountains to where his collaborator was summering to consult with him on the final selection. One evening Hebart entered the cottage to find Vivian alone. He extended his arms to her and she had run to him. The beginning of the betrayal had been as simple as that.

She had never told Larry what she had expected of their marriage; it was the sort of thing one couldn't put into words. But she had believed that he had understood that her love should have some kind of issue. No, not a child. That surely she didn't want for a moment. A life. She could scarcely make it more specific. It had seemed to her that so intellectual and gifted a man ought to mold her into something useful. She was aware that she was totally amorphous, that she had too many talents. She painted, wrote poetry, acted in amateur theatricals, and none of these occupations were vitally important to her. Desire floated through her consciousness and shifted her attention from one object to another. The fact was that she couldn't really be serious. But that apparently didn't worry Larry. When she mentioned her own defects, he laughed. He was intuitive about her moods but not what produced them. Wit and soundness he thought could cure what she recognized as a chronic disease. She was weary of living on the surface of life; she had to penetrate more deeply.

Hebart standing before her naked, his scars exposed, had seemed to understand. That had been at the beginning when he had still spoken as if they were about to run away together. "That nothing has touched you," he said, "is not at all surprising. How could you have felt very deeply when there was nothing to respond to? What happens to you? You live all your life in a nice bourgeois home, go away to college, and get a crush on your teacher. That's your only experience, and bang, you're married." Vivian realized the truth of this assessment. She felt contrition for having behaved so stupidly. What a mess she had made of her life. Something had to be done to correct the error. But, as Hebart pointed out, divorce was possible. . . .

They were out of the woods, at the edge of the clearing where Hebart's cottage was. The fire near the lake lit up the faces of laughing people. Stars shone overhead. The moon was battling to throw off its blanket of clouds, had tinged the black mass with a vibrant orange. Vivian for an instant was caught in the wonder of so much beauty. It seemed as if what she was seeing was more real than the horror she felt. If she could become only eyes perpetually watching. . . . Larry said, "I don't know why you want to take such risks. You know you are carrying a child."

They walked slowly toward the gathering. It seemed so joyous, the voices so alive with pleasure, one could not believe there was any deception in them. But at the heart of that gaiety Vivian knew that Hebart stood. Then at last she caught sight of him among the gay whirling shadows.

He had on white flannels and a blue serge coat, conservatively elegant as always. It had been a combination of that elegance and his enormous size which had first attracted her. But now, towering above his guests, he looked monstrous to her. A giant. An absurd creature out of some fairy tale, to whom she had entrusted her heart. It was strange how quickly one's vision altered; a few days before she had still considered him remarkable. There was no doubt that he was the center of all this activity. Standing near the fire, he shot out comments in a booming voice and when he spoke everyone strained to listen. Vivian wanted to laugh. Hebart had only contempt for these people whom he had overawed. He considered them *genus academicus*, a particularly ludicrous variety. Many times with her in his arms he had explained to her how they attempted to substitute scholarship for life. But if they were dead so was he. No, he wasn't a man. He was a corpse only partially revivified. She thought of the network of scars on his body, shrapnel wounds he had received during the war. Why had ugliness seemed so romantic to her? These were not the stigmata of Christ. Nor was the glint in his dead glass eye the stare of divinity. There was something ridiculous Vivian sensed, in all her attachments. Life kept beckoning to her, and all she found was death.

"Hi there, Viv," Bob Williamson said as soon as he caught sight of her. He taught French at Princetown, had done his thesis on the Symbolistes. Alice Watkins walked over to shake her hand; Alice's husband's specialty was Chaucer. The colony was almost completely academic; Hebart was the exception, the great man, the brainy fellow who wandered about doing as he pleased, philosophizing about existence. For eighteen years he had lived in Europe, and had grown to despise America. He had an international reputation. Vivian looked straight ahead to where he stood and thought she saw his gaze shift slightly. He left the fire and moved toward her. She saw him as a Cyclops approaching, arrogant and one-eyed.

"Well, I'm delighted," he said, taking her hand. "We'd almost given you up." The phonograph on the porch suddenly broke into song, "Oh, you're driving me crazy."

"I guess we lost track of the time," Vivian answered.

He called for a drink for her and then said, "Come on over and have a hamburger."

"What was he thinking?" she wondered. Did he believe she had come to entreat him to take her away? She supposed he regarded her with the same contempt as he did the others. One of the little people who lacked the courage to live. The day before he had told her to be sensible. He existed from hand to mouth on the smallest of legacies. Marriage wasn't feasible for him. He had to be unencumbered; he thought he had made that clear. Next year he would try to get back and they would start seeing each other again. Vivian supposed he had a peasant girl in every village. That was what she had been for him, a pretty number of the peasantry.

They walked to the fire and he put meat on a bun.

"What will you have on it?" he asked. "We have onion, relish, and catsup."

Vivian took the hamburger plain.

As she bit into the sandwich, she noticed Larry standing with Williamson and Alice Watkins. He felt most at home with such people, individuals like himself who were concerned with who published where and what feuds had arisen within the teaching community. A man like Hebart terrified him. When Hebart spoke, Larry said, "Is that so? Really." He listened attentively to the other grandiose theories, nodding his head. Vivian knew he was impressed but certainly no convert. "An interesting man," he had said to her a number of times. His most scathing criticism had been, "What he says may be true, but I'm not certain that it's as sure as he makes it out to be." Vivian had argued with him. It was she who had become the convert. Larry she had decided, was jealous, and at any rate too small to appreciate her lover's greatness. Larry's concern was poetry whose doctrines he did not believe and which he regarded as beautiful because of the adequacy of the expression. In those far away days when her heart had fluttered seeing him in front of the class, she had not known that his world was such a trivial business. What she had done was to confuse Wordsworth's and Coleridge's vision with his. She had believed that through Larry the universe was divulging its secret. She had made a mistake, it seemed; mistakes were her specialty. The child that she was carrying under her heart was also an error. As she stood next to the fire she watched Hebart's restless eyes moving and sensed that he was looking for someone to bait. His mind was more agile than theirs and consequently it was not difficult for him to humiliate them.

No, the child could not be moving. The cells which had so recently joined had as yet created only the smallest of embryos. Life was growing in her silently, life which she didn't understand. As yet it had not acquired its own motion. It was forming in her body to replace her, ir-rationally demanding birth. Soon it would be man or woman. But the all-seeing Hebart knew nothing of it. The bath of fire which had almost destroyed him and which he said had given him deeper insight, hadn't made him so much of a demigod that he did not have to be told such simple facts. The hint of a smile appeared on Vivian's lips. "Bill," she said, "I have something to tell you."

He turned back to the fire and the roasting meat. "What do you think of this batch? I guess they're done."

"Walk down to the lake with me. You'll find it in-teresting."

It had been her intention never to let him know. In her first anger, pride in the ascendant, she had determined to never see him nor communicate with him again. But now she realized that it was right that he learn of it and be forced to ponder and guess even though it could never be as it was for her. They stood in the silence of the night and she knew that his composure was shattered.

"You're absolutely sure of this, Vivian?" he asked.

She shrugged her shoulders. "There isn't any doubt."

"But you must have taken precautions.'

"I always do."

"Can you fix the time?"

"How is that possible?"

"Let me think about it. It's a shock. What have you told Larry?"

"He's certain the child is his."

Hebart, she saw, was too wily to irritate her by disowning responsibility immediately.

"We'd better go back," he said. "It'll look funny if we're away too long."

Now he was getting cautious. While the affair had been going on, he'd been willing to take inordinate risks.

"Don't worry," Vivian said. "I have no intention of denouncing you."

"Honest to goodness, Vivian, I never thought of anything of the kind."

"Well, you have," she said. "You can rest easy there."

As they came back into the light of the fire, it was a joy to her to see the pallor of his face. He looked as if that shell which had fractured him had fallen again. He had told her that sometimes he had nightmares, since it was impossible to conquer the irrational mind completely. Well, now he was dreaming his nightmare awake. God, let it continue; she was surely suffering enough. There were no illusions to protect her.

She saw Larry and realized that he had been looking for her. He walked over and reached for her hand; she did not deny it to him.

"We walked down by the lake," she said. "It's heavenly there."

Why didn't the choking sensation in her throat go? She was afraid she was going to cry.

Larry turned to Hebart. "How's the new article coming, Bill?"

For the first time he was embarrassed in Larry's presence, Vivian noticed. Hebart's answer was noncommittal, an attempt at brush-off.

Larry laughed. "Well, I'm happy to learn that even you have difficulty writing sometimes."

Williamson joined them.

"In a few days you'll be in Europe, away from us barbarians," Williamson said.

"Yes," Hebart answered.

In a few days, Vivian thought, the summer would have vanished for him. He would not return next year. Now there was a good reason for him not to come.

"Things are clearer over there," she remarked. "The human spirit has been less tampered with."

Larry shot her a look. Williamson laughed. "I thought you were a supporter of Bill's. Don't I detect irony, Vivian?"

There was a wildness in her eyes. She laughed.

"Oh, I am. I know that everything he tells us is gospel."

Larry looked at her again. She was aware that she ought to control her tongue.

"What are you talking about?" Alice Watkins asked as she joined the circle.

"I think it's the birth of the new spirit," Williamson said, laughing. "Isn't that what we've been talking about all summer? Apparently we agree that if it isn't stillborn, it'll be alive. Other than that, we're still at swords' points. Bill, would you say that's a correct summation?"

Hebart said that it was.

"Oh," Alice Watkins said, making a face, "it's all too deep for me."

"Well, I find Bill plausible enough when I read him," Williamson continued. "My difficulty is to make it apply. You know we just aren't going to get a classical renaissance, Bill. It isn't in the cards."

"I'm not saying what we ought to get. I'm saying what ought to be."

Vivian's impression was that Hebart only spoke because he feared that silence on his part would seem odd.

"All right. We're decadents and savages besides," Williamson said. "Our art is too emotive, our thought too sentimental. We can't transcend our petty natures. We're not Athenians and do not understand the golden mean. But for the moment we're all that there is."

Hebart stared at him coldly. "I don't deny that." The

contempt had come back to his face. She had touched him for a moment but already he was forgetting, under Williamson's attack was once more marshalling his forces. His one good eye flashed with anger. These people didn't understand, couldn't understand; they were too puny. But Hebart would do his best to make it clear to them, that was his job. True. Life was life and certain of its terms could not be changed, but you could determine how you wanted to live. You didn't have to be a pig. There had been men who had transcended their torments, who had looked reality in the face and had willed to live both heroically and joyously. "Joyously," Hebart screamed, carried away by his rhetoric. "What's wrong with joy? Why do you people refuse it?"

Vivian started to giggle and then laugh unrestrainedly. Hebart looked so grotesque with one dead eye in his head, yelling for joy. Startled, everyone looked at her.

"I think we should go home, Vivian," Larry said, pulling her to one side. "We probably shouldn't have come in the first place. It's been too much for you."

"No, I'm all right. It's just that it's so funny."

Larry looked at her quizzically. "What's so funny? I don't see."

"But of course you do. You know he's got a glass eye."

"I mean he talks all that nonsense and he can hardly see."

"Are you all right, Vivian?" Alice Watkins asked, coming over.

Vivian started to laugh again. "The whole summer we've been listening to that corpse as if he really knew something. I don't doubt that we should have compassion. But you don't go to a basket case to get your vision of the world."

"What's he done that's so terrible?" Alice Watkins argued. "All right, he wants us to be joyful. I would be if I could. But it's nothing to get upset about."

"He wants to kill us," Vivian said. "We're just dung that he tramples on."

"Vivian is tired," Larry explained as more and more people gathered. "She's been under something of a strain lately. We're going home now."

"I'm not tired, Larry."

"Come along, Vivian."

She pulled herself from him, began denouncing Hebart again. Hebart stood a few feet away, his back to the group. Vivian's voice grew louder and louder.

Larry said nothing to her on the way home and that frightened her. She knew that in making a spectacle of herself she had disgraced them both. Now all those who lived at the edge of the lake were discussing her conduct. The story probably would be that she had got drunk.

Well, she did feel tipsy, but not from alcohol. Her skin was so hot, she wondered if she had a fever.

Larry opened the door of the cottage for her and she preceded him in.

"I don't want to talk tonight, Larry," she said. "I've got to go straight to bed."

"Calm down, Vivian. You can't go on this way."

"I don't want to talk," she repeated.

"What's been going on between you and Hebart?"

She stopped and turned.

"Are you making an accusation?"

He was doing his best to control himself she could see. But there was a plaintive, hurt look on his face.

"I'm not dumb, Vivian. I've seen what's been going on this summer."

"You have? Well, what has been going on?"

"Sit down, Vivian," Larry pleaded. "We're adults. We can talk. I'm not going to hurt you. I just want to know what's bothering you."

She stood cold and frozen, wondering how much he had actually guessed. "You said something about Hebart."

"I want to put water on for tea. Get out of your clothes and then we'll talk."

One of those terrible moments had again come in her life, which were forever marring it. They had been happening since her childhood. Lies she had been caught in. Enemies confronting her. It was like Hebart being nailed down by his shell. One suffered terribly. She went into the bedroom and undressed slowly. There was only one solution. Larry and she must be divorced. He entered the bedroom carrying a cup of tea.

"Before you say anything," she said, "there's something I want to say." He nodded his head and sat down on the bed. "Larry, I want a divorce. Will you give it to me?"

He smiled. "I thought you'd say that."

"Will you give it to me?"

He didn't answer immediately, sat stirring the tea in his cup. There was about him now a dignity and reserve that she hadn't found in him in years. He seemed once again the brilliant young man standing in front of the class and with whom she had fallen in love.

"Vivian," he said, "there were a lot of my friends who thought I was making a mistake in marrying you. They said you were a romantic kid who didn't have the remotest idea of what was going on. And in a way you were and I knew it. You listened to the poetry and you thought I could take you somewhere that I couldn't. But who can? Hebart? Vivian, you're in the midst of life, and you've got to live it."

"I want a divorce, Larry," she said. "I don't want to argue."

"What are you going to do? Marry Hebart? Does he know?"

"I don't want to discuss it."

"What about the child?"

"I don't want the child."

"So everything's to be killed," he said. "Vivian, are you willing to take such responsibility?"

It was at that moment that she started to cry. She threw her head on the pillow and closed her eyes. What Larry said was the truth. She was a killer like Hebart.

"Stop it, Vivian. What good's that? It's my fault too. I saw the way things were going and I said nothing. I said to myself—this one will pass too. You know all through the years I've permitted myself to be humiliated. I've watched you prance through drawing room after drawing room, looking for a new saviour. Vivian, you wear them out so quickly. If we yield to you, you discover that we're human. Tell me one thing. Is the child his?"

"No, no," she screamed, raising her head.

"Do you swear that it isn't?"

She looked away from him and didn't answer.

"You don't know whose it is? How disgusting."

Through her tears she recognized the disgust on his face. He was pale, too, and the teacup rattled in his hand. She watched as he placed it slowly on the floor.

Then he stood up, paced back and forth, arguing with himself.

"What are you going to do?" she asked sullenly, at the same time knowing that she was actually waiting for him to tell her that she did not know how she felt. She, and not he, had remained the adolescent, she realized. Had she ever been able to make a decision? The future had always tormented her. The saviour she had looked for was to have been someone who would explain away the darkness. But they had all abandoned her.

"I won't give you a divorce, Vivian," he said, as the tears flowed down her cheeks once more.

His large gray eyes were full of despair. "What would you do? Were would you go?" he asked. "Surely not to Hebart, that joy-lover! No, I'm afraid you'll have to stay here with me. Perhaps, after the child is born . . ." His voice trailed off and he left the room quickly; the door slammed with finality. He had not noticed that she was shivering.

For a while she sat on the bed, gripping her arms and pressing them against her abdomen. Then, still shivering, she slipped beneath the covers. But she could not bring herself to turn off the light.

# The New Man

Linda Herman stayed late that night typing correspondence she had not completed during the day. Her alternative had been dinner with her family and she had decided that she was in no mood to bicker. Ever since Linda had turned eighteen, her mother had found her incomprehensible. Typing was a skill Linda had only recently acquired and her fingers remained awkward. She was annoyed to discover that she was hitting wrong keys and having to erase. Once or twice she swore out loud, noting that smudges were appearing on the paper. She wondered if she ought not pull out the sheet and start all over again.

There was a knock on the door and Linda looked up surprised; she had thought that she was alone in the office. "Yes?" she said, turning her head in the direction of the sound. The door opened slowly and the new man came in.

"I'm not interrupting?" he inquired in his usual solicitous manner.

"Oh, it's nothing important, Mr. Wilbur. I was just finishing up some letters."

As the new man entered the room, he continued to apologize. Linda had heard him ramble on like this before and she sensed that she was in for it. He sat down in a chair opposite her and smiled wistfully.

"You're new here, too, aren't you?" he asked.

"Yes," she answered.

She had arrived at Grayson's three weeks before; it was only her second job but she had found no difficulty in getting herself accepted by the other employees. No one but Mr. Grayson, the president, liked the new man. He had been brought in by executive decree to improve the business's efficiency. From the very first he had snooped about investigating what everyone was doing and offering comments. Presumably he wanted to be tactful and always apologized while he was making his suggestions. Whatever he said took an hour; no one escaped his tentative, embarrassed criticism. Linda wondered when he would start peeking at the letters she was doing.

"It isn't always easy to fit in," the new man said crossing his legs, "particularly when you have a difficult job to do."

"No, it isn't," Linda agreed, and kept her hands stubbornly on the keyboard.

It wasn't only that the new man was officious; his appearance was against him as well. He was more a photograph than a person. As soon as you looked at him, you thought he should be on a subway poster commenting on the brand of whiskey he drank. This evening he was as handsome and as uncreased as ever. Nearly fifty, he was more than twice Linda's age, but in some respects he seemed younger. His face was almost that of a boy's, not a single line on it, but unlike a boy's it exhibited neither joy nor sorrow. Linda at twenty-two was totally responsive to everything. At the moment she was annoyed that the new man had interrupted her and there was a sullen, trapped look in her brilliant blue eyes.

The new man was apparently unaware of her attitude. He kept surveying her handsome young face and her disheveled young hair and then said suddenly, "What do you want to work for? The day's over. Come on out and I'll buy you dinner."

Linda flushed.

"Oh, I'm sorry," she lied. "I have a date."

"Well, some other time. It's just that I'm down tonight. I've had bad news."

"Oh, I'm sorry, Mr. Wilbur."

The new man continued to smile. Linda wondered what the bad news could be.

"You don't think we might have a quick drink?" the new man asked.

"All right, a quick one. I'll go and tidy up."

She rose from the typewriter and walked down the hall to the washroom. Linda was a rangy girl, somewhat hoidenish in appearance. In her teens she had been a tomboy, but at college she had had her intellectual awakening and her rebellion against the society and now she was more interested in the things of the mind than in sports. Though she was liked at Grayson's, she was considered a trifle odd, coming to work as she did in a sport jacket and strange blouses and skirts. There was a rumor around the office that she wrote and was making notes on what happened at Grayson's. The firm published music, so she was not absolutely out of place.

There had been several men already in her life, all of whom had turned out to be disappointments. Her mother said that she could not be satisfied, that her eyes were forever on the stars. But Linda wasn't going to compromise because of her mother's opinions. She wanted to experience the deepest love possible. So far the men she had known had been too mundane and tame. That was why she was dateless that evening. She had turned down a couple of offers.

But, as she stood powdering her face in the washroom, she had to admit to herself that anything would have been more exciting than the new man. She had allowed herself to get "conned" into the drink. Probably nothing very bad had happened to him.

He was still smiling when she returned.

"Ready so soon?" he asked briskly.

"Yes," she answered as she slipped into her tan sport jacket.

"Here, permit me," he said quickly, not allowing her to open the door by herself.

It was as if he had memorized the motions of an actor in a sophisticated comedy. He was all turns and twists and bows, gallantry carried to the point of absurdity. Everything was a gesture; as they walked to the bar, he persisted in slipping from one side of her to the other to make sure that he walked next to the curb. Linda got dizzy watching him. Nor did he stop talking while he maneuvered. He spoke about what a wonderful man Mr. Grayson was and about the merits of everyone else in the office. There was not a single person connected with the business whom he did not have a high opinion of, although he was aware that he had not as yet been accepted as one of "the team." "Tell me, Miss Herman," he said, "give me your frank opinion: where have I gone wrong?"

Linda bit her lip. "Honestly, Mr. Wilbur, as far as I know they all like you."

"You've heard no talk?"

"I don't mingle with many of the people."

The new man nodded his head but the smile did not leave his face. He had probably taken her out to pump her and she was determined to give no information. The more she was with him, the more she disliked him. She decided that she would order a martini, drink it quickly, and then break away.

Finally they arrived at the bar which was introduced by the new man appropriately. "You'll find it a splendid place. I've been coming here for years. Guido—that's the owner—is one of the most engaging people I've ever met.' He opened the door. "Hello, Peter," and he gave the bartender an imperial wave. No sooner had they sat down and ordered than he said he had to make a telephone call. "To the airport," he explained. "I must see whether they could get my reservations."

Linda's martini arrived before the new man's return. She sat sipping the drink, trying to imagine what it was like to be him. Around the office he was called "a son of a bitch." Clearly that was not his view of himself.

When he returned, the smile on his face had become broader. "Well, I go at midnight," he announced as he sat down. "They're very efficient, aren't they?—I mean the airplane people. I really put them to a great deal of bother."

"How?" Linda inquired. Presumably all he had done was reserve space.

"Well, it's quite a complicated operation. You see, I have to go to a small town in Arizona. It requires two changes. They've synchronized things perfectly."

"You're going on business?" Linda asked casually.

"No." The new man smiled blandly. "I must attend a funeral."

So there had been bad news. Linda lowered her voice. "Someone you knew well?"

"My son's," the new man said.

Linda put down her glass quickly. "Oh, Mr. Wilbur, I'm terribly sorry."

"Well, that's the way it is," the new man said. "His mother called this morning. An auto accident! Killed instantly. I'm glad at any rate that he didn't suffer."

"Yes," Linda said, still breathless. "How old was he?"

The new man put his elbows on the table and appeared to be cogitating.

"Nineteen, I think," and then he quickly corrected himself. "No, twenty. He had his birthday two months ago."

"They've been out there vacationing?"

"Oh, no," the new man said, shaking his head emphatically. "That's where she lives. You must understand she's not my wife any longer. We've been divorced for years."

Linda didn't know what to say and busied herself once more with her drink. The new man appeared to accept his son's death with such equanimity. He drew out his wallet with a flourish and extended it toward her. "Would you like to see his picture?"

Linda said that she would.

"There," the new man said and he pointed. Linda looked quickly at the snapshot and saw a trim young man dressed in riding pants and a polo shirt, standing next to a horse. The image frightened her; the young man in the picture no longer existed. She shook her head. "It's awful, Mr. Wilbur, just awful. When did you see him last?"

The new man fumbled in his pocket and brought out a package of cigarettes.

"It's a damned shame," he said in a level voice. "Life is tough. I've been at one end of the  continent and she's been at the other. You know how things are. I've always wanted to get out there, but I couldn't. It's been at least five years."

Linda shivered hearing this confession. She raised her drink to her lips and drained down the contents.

"Have another," the new man said quickly.

"Really, Mr. Wilbur, I should be going."

"Another five minutes won't make any difference."

"All right," Linda said, "but this will be the last."

Music had begun in the bar, soft and sentimental; Linda had the impression that the new man was listening to the tunes even as he spoke. Nor was she wrong, for he suddenly asked, "That's a nice one, isn't it? I caught the show a few weeks ago. Did you see it?" Linda didn't know what show was being referred to. He told her its name and said she must be sure not to miss it. "Oh, it's not profound," he added apologetically, "but everything doesn't have to be serious. I like a trifle now and then that takes your mind off things."

"There's nothing wrong with that," Linda said. It seemed to her that the smile on the new man's face had become more defensive.

"You're not always reading books?" he asked.

She laughed, "Oh no, scarcely."

"Well, I wasn't sure. It's hard to know another person. I thought maybe you didn't like me because I'm not an intellectual. Do you like me, Linda?"

"Why, of course, Mr. Wilbur."

He stared across the table at her as if trying to determine the degree of her hypocrisy. "Maybe you do.

139

Maybe you don't. But I'm going to tell you something that will shock you. I'm being perfectly frank. My son's death disturbs me but I'm not shattered. That is shocking, isn't it? But be logical about it. After the break-up I only saw the boy a half-dozen times. He was practically a stranger to me."

Linda lowered her eyes. She wished that the new man would stop undressing before her.

He looked at her sharply. "It would be wrong of me to pretend to feel something that I don't, wouldn't it?"

Linda kept her eyes averted. "Yes, I suppose so, Mr. Wilbur."

He laughed nervously. "Why be formal? Call me Rob."

"All right, Rob. The fact is I've never been in your position. I don't know how I would feel."

"No, you're young," he said. "You have your life before you. If Eleanor and I had stayed together, it would have been different."

It was, Linda realized, an introduction to the story of his life. He had to exhibit himself; he was a compulsive talker.

He had had three marriages, he explained, and none of them had worked out. But he didn't blame any of the women. Perhaps he had done something wrong. He supposed he had, although he couldn't imagine what. His first wife and he hadn't even quarreled. He had believed they were getting along handsomely until he had returned home one evening to discover that she had run away with another man. The second had been much more of a fault-finder, a sharp-tongued woman who, a few months after their marriage, had discovered that she couldn't abide with him. "To me," he said, "her criticisms never meant anything. Is there anything wrong in being courteous? You have to be in my job. You notice how careful I've been around the office, and still I've made enemies. If I'd been rude, I'd really be hated. Isn't that so?"

Linda said that it was.

"Anyway, I think you should be kind to everyone. I'm polite to those who are near to me and I'm polite to strangers. That's the way I was brought up to be. Tell me, Linda, do you think I'm too polite?"

"No, Rob." She had finished her second drink but didn't have the nerve to suggest leaving. The new man noticed that her glass was empty and motioned to the waiter. Although the smile remained on his face, his eyes had become hard and angry. He was remembering how outrageously he had been treated.

"It was business," he continued, "that ruined my third marriage. My wife was young, much younger than I, and very impressionable. You know what my business is, don't you? I'm an expert on businesses. Whether you sell post cards or tractors, the theory of business is all the same. Your task is to sell at the optimum price so as to make the maximum amount of profit. There's no sentiment in it. The balance sheet tells the story. You've seen how it is at Grayson's. They're all good men but the slaves of habit. Because something's been done a certain way for twenty-five years doesn't mean that it's right. But as soon as you suggest a change, you're treading on someone's toes." The new man shook his head sadly. "I try to be polite, but wherever I go I make enemies. And when you cross people, they can be treacherous. The trouble with Alma was that she believed the stories that were circulated about me. I don't want to hurt anyone. If someone loses his job, it's not my fault. There's not a single business that I've been in that hasn't benefited from having me around. I could show you letters praising me to the skies. And what do I get out of it? As soon as I straighten out a corporation, I move on to another."

Linda thought of what was said in the office. The charge there was that the new man was a superficial sycophant. Each day he rushed to Mr. Grayson's office to explain his findings. He thought that perhaps the Bach chorales ought to be bound with the Beethoven piano sonatas. He had an idea that Saint-Saëns and Debussy together would make an excellent package. Knowing nothing of music, there was no barbarism of which he was not capable. The problem was that Mr. Grayson, the last in a long line of Graysons, knew no more about music than did the new manager. Working together, they were determined to make the company modern. As yet no heads had fallen, but inevitably they would. The old hands at Grayson's, seeing customs and attitudes attacked that they considered sacred, were not as polite as the new man. The more powerful railed against him publicly. In a sense, the action had acquired the fervor of a religious war. At present a significant battle was being waged over the covers in which the music was bound. The new man said that the designs in use were stodgy and old-fashioned, and pointed out that sex was valuable even in the merchandising of plain songs. It was self-evident to him that those who were interested in music would disregard the cover designs; the new man wanted to develop additional markets. There had never been any doubt on which side Linda was in this struggle; it was only the new man's bereavement that kept her from speaking out now. But when he had the temerity to launch a covert attack against her own boss, Harry Axelrod, she lost her temper. "Honestly, Rob, you talk as if only one position was possible. The situation at Grayson's is very complicated."

143

"Don't get angry, Linda," he said softly. "Temper doesn't solve anything."

"Well, some of the people in the office feel very strongly about what's been going on."

"Then, you think I'm in the wrong."

"They love what they're doing."

The new man shrugged his shoulders. "Tell me where I'm in error."

"I've got to go, Rob. I'm late already."

"No, you've advanced a point of view and now you should substantiate it."

"We were only going to have one quick drink, remember?"

The new man smiled shyly. "Is this date of yours so important? Can't you break it?"

"No, I can't." She reached for her pocketbook.

"Please, Linda. I don't want to have dinner alone tonight." She knew he was throwing himself on her mercy. "Please. Please."

She wanted to get up and run out of the bar but was restrained by the look of desperation in the new man's eyes. After all he wasn't a dog. He was all too human.

"Well, let's have it somewhere in the neighborhood," she said tartly. "I've got to be home early."

"My plane leaves at midnight," he reminded her.

:

The term "neighborhood" she soon found out was extremely ambiguous. The new man would have liked to drive up to Westchester. He finally settled for a place within the city limits but did insist on getting his car which was at a parking lot near the office and had to be removed before his airplane journey. On the way to the restaurant he suddenly remembered there was something he had to buy, and parked on one of the main streets.

"It won't take a minute," he said. "I'll be back before you finish your cigarette."

When he returned, he was carrying a corsage of orchids.

"You've been so very kind," he said. "I hope you'll accept them."

It would have been too awkard to have said no. Linda permitted him to pin them on her blouse.

"Rob," she said, "let's not go to a fancy place. You can see how I'm dressed."

"You're a young princess," he assured her. "You don't have to worry about clothes. I'm going to take you to a place such as you've never seen before."

The restaurant was in the East Fifties and was not, as she had anticipated, one that catered to international playboys and demimondes. She had heard it spoken of as a gourmet's paradise and had always wondered whether food could actually be worth what it costs there. Any other time she would have enjoyed having such an interesting experience, but the situation in which she found herself, dressed inappropriately and in the company of such an obnoxious escort, cancelled for her any possible pleasure. She saw immediately that the new man was well known there. The hat check girl smiled at him and the headwaiter addressed him by name. No one appeared to be staring at her but she resented the possibility of being thought the new man's girl. It was a relief to find that none of the tables were of the sort where the couple sits side by side.

"Nice, isn't it?" the new man asked as soon as they were seated.

Linda nodded her head and then refused his offer of another drink. He leaned over, smiling at her. "Now what about Grayson's? Suppose you were in charge, what would you do?"

Ever since the appearance of the orchids, the erotic tinge to the evening had become more noticeable. Linda knew that she was having an effect upon the new man. But the timetable was such that she was in little danger; he had to be on that plane at midnight. She decided that it would be coarse to exhibit an emotion that she did not feel, but could see no reason why she should not be diplomatic in presenting the view that was held by the majority at Grayson's. Women had many times exerted a subtle influence upon important events. Linda had the urge to try her hand at being masterful.

"I'm not saying that all your ideas are wrong, Rob, but put yourself in the position of the people at Grayson's. Some of them have been there for thirty or forty years. And one must admit that in many ways they're very accomplished."

"I'm not denying that, Linda."

"Henry Axelrod, for example, is very well thought of in the trade. He has connections everywhere. He's very valuable."

"My dear, didn't I say exactly that?"

"Well, you are polite, Rob, but nevertheless you rub people the wrong way. I know you mean well and I'm sure that everyone at Grayson's knows that too, but when they say that Debussy and Saint-Saëns ought not to be in the same volume, they have certain reasons which may not be immediately obvious to you."

"What reasons?"

"Well, they're composers of such different tendencies."

"They are," the new man said. "Well, why didn't someone tell me?"

Linda remembered that Henry Axelrod had spent an hour talking about French musical history, but evidently the new man had not been listening. Now, however, as she spoke, he hung on every word.

"It's somewhat the same with the Bach chorales and the Beethoven sonatas."

The new man's eyes began to sparkle.

"You're magnificent, Linda," he said, "simply magnificent."

Linda plodded on. "As far as the covers go, they could be improved, but I don't think quite in the direction you've suggested."

"What direction?"

"Well, I'd have to show you."

"Linda," the new man said. "Why don't you help me? Between the two of us we could really renovate Grayson's."

Linda paled. The new man was looking at her so intently.

"I could manage it," he assured her. "You know I have influence with George Grayson. Say the word and you can be my assistant."

Linda shook her head. "No, Rob. Honestly, I'm not equipped for it."

He reached his hand across the table trying to touch her. She drew back.

"I think you're better equipped than you believe you are."

"Rob," she said, "we haven't ordered. Your plane leaves at midnight."

He called for the bill of fare.

"I realize how terrible you must feel," she said, "having to face that trip." She had come to the conclusion that it was inadvisable to talk further about Grayson's. "What an awful thing for you and your ex-wife to meet again under such circumstances."

"That's true," he agreed and began advising her on what to eat.

"It can't help but bring back a thousand memories. I suppose you loved her a great deal once." Under other circumstances Linda would have been attempting to get the bereaved man's mind off of the past. But here the opposite was necessary.

"It's funny," he said. "I've almost forgotten how she looks. Yes, I guess I loved her a lot."

"Where did you live?" Linda asked. "Were you New Yorkers?"

"No, Californians."

"Los Angeles?"

"Yes."

The waiter came and the new man gave their order.

"It will be painful going there," he said, returning his attention to her, "very painful. For one so young you're very perceptive. All of those hours alone on the plane. I don't like being alone, do you Linda?"

"It all depends," Linda answered.

149

"What do you think about when you're alone?"

"Oh, lots of things."

There was a strange expression on the new man's face. He lowered his voice to a whisper, "Linda, why don't you come with me?"

"Go with you? Rob, you're crazy."

"I'll only be out at the house for a few hours. You can wait at the airport. I'm not going to hang around. Then we can fly on to San Francisco."

"Aren't you going to attend the burial?"

"Well, you could put up at a hotel."

Linda's face became masklike. "What are you going for?"

The new man gestured with his hands. "It wouldn't look right for me not to show up. Don't worry about your job. I'll fix it with Grayson."

"Thank you just the same, Rob." She was attempting to keep control of herself.

"I've insulted you, haven't I?"

"Not necessarily."

The new man gave her his broadest smile and said, "I was only testing you."

"Testing me! What kind of a test was that?"

"You don't hold yourself cheaply. When you get married, you'll be a splendid wife. You're loyal. I like

the way you stood up for Henry Axelrod. You're wonderful now; in a few years you'll be tremendous."

"Thank you, Rob."

"Ah, if I'd only met someone like you twenty years
ago. Life tends to make you cynical. You begin to think
that everyone can be bought. It's refreshing to come
across someone who can't be."

"I don't know that I'm such a paragon."

"You're too young to understand what you are, Linda.
There's a song that's called, 'You Are Love.' You must
know it. That's what you are, Linda, pure love. Don't
ever change. I know everything about you. All you need
is to be put through the fire and tempered a little. Linda,
come on that plane with me and we'll be married in San
Francisco. I may be older than you but I can help you a
lot. You're the kind of girl who needs an older man. I'm
serious about what I said before. Between the two of us
we could run Grayson's."

"Honestly, Rob, this isn't the time to talk about something like that."

"It's the right time. In a way my son's death has shaken
me up."

"But you just told me that you scarcely knew him."

"That's true, but I knew he was there and he was mine.
Now I have absolutely no one."

"You'll find someone. Really, I'm not right for you."

"You are right for me. I need you, Linda."

She bowed her head and stared down at the table. "I just can't marry you, Rob."

His face had grayed as in a painting where imperfect colors have been used. It seemed to Linda that he was in the process of disappearing.

"It's horrible to get old," he said violently, "just horrible."

Linda's eyes teared. She reached over and touched the new man's hand. "Oh, come on now, Rob. You're not very old."

"Don't you believe that, Linda. I'm ancient. I have nothing. I don't care what they do at Grayson's. What's that place mean to me?"

"But you're doing such a fine job. All you have to do is learn a little about the business."

"Grayson's is a laugh," the new man said. "They've all been laughs—every damned business I've been in. You spend your life doing nothing and then you're dead."

Linda's existence, despite its travails, shimmered with meaning. She wandered about the city going to art galleries and listening to concerts. She worried about the world and propagandized against war. There was scarcely an issue that did not excite her. It was difficult for her to believe that the new man found everything such a total blank. Her duty, she saw, was to show him his error.

During the rest of dinner she tried to suggest various therapies. If he took a course in music, she pointed out, Grayson's might become more comprehensible to him. Or, if he didn't want to study music, he could try literature.

"If I signed up for something, would you go with me?"

"We'll see about that," she answered.

She realized that she wasn't making much headway with him. Golf he sort of liked, but you couldn't play it all the time. It was also fun to gamble. He enjoyed dancing. But though he didn't mention it, she knew what he liked best. She wondered how many other women he had had beside the three wives. Love! But he didn't mean the same thing by love that she did. Yes, in a way, he was right; she was love. It quivered in her body. It was alive in her. Sometimes it made her sad and desperate but she was sure that the time would come when it would justify itself.

"Well, shall we go?" he finally asked, calling for the check. She was aware that as far as he was concerned the evening had been a failure.

When they reached the car, he said, "You live down in the Village, don't you?"

"Yes," she answered and she gave him the address.

"Well, we didn't become friends, did we?" he remarked as soon as the car had begun to move.

"Oh, I wouldn't say that."

They drove several blocks in silence and then he pulled the car up to the curb and stopped. He reached for her and caught her by the wrists.

"Linda," he said, "you're young. One kiss won't hurt you."

She struggled to release herself. "Rob, I'm going to get out of the car."

"Only one kiss. That's all I'm asking."

They were down near the docks. There were no lights in the warehouses. The sidewalks were deserted.

"Rob," she said, "let me go."

"Ah, come on, Linda, who are you kidding? You've had men before."

He pulled her to him and pressed his mouth down on her lips. She tried to scream. His hands were all over her. In the night the only sound she could hear was his breathing. It seemed to her as if the most important thing in life was to deny herself to him. They were in darkness. She continued to kick and struggle.

A light passed across the windshield and lit up the interior. The new man turned his head. A truck was passing. Linda pulled at his hands, freed herself for an instant, and screamed. The new man turned his head back to her and asked, "What did you do that for?"

Now his hands no longer held her. She opened the

door and jumped from the car. She started to run, and then, looking back over her shoulder, saw that the car was following her. She veered, darted across the street; the car accelerated. It was coming straight at her. She screamed again. There was the sound of brakes and then the new man's voice, "You sure are a dumb girl, Linda. I hope I don't find you at Grayson's when I get back."

The motor roared and the car shot past her. She started to run and the shadows pressed in on her. No, she must never see that face again. Never. But it appeared to be lurking everywhere. As she hurried past the warehouses, she trembled. What did he want with her? Why didn't he find himself some cheap woman? Only when she reached an avenue down which traffic was pouring did she slow her pace. She saw an empty taxi and hailed it. But the address she gave the driver was not her own but her parents'. She feared that the new man waited for her at the apartment, ready to leap out and rape her.

The world settled back into place as soon as they crossed the park and came to Fifth Avenue. The sight of the fortress-gray buildings calmed her. She was back in civilization. The doorman helped her out of the cab.

"Good evening, Miss Herman."

"Good evening, Jerry."

When her mother threw open the door, she was asked

immediately, "Well, to what do we owe this unexpected visit?"

Linda said that she had been lonely and had come home to sleep.

Her mother laughed. "I don't know why you ever took that apartment when you have a perfectly good place here."

"Mother," Linda said, "I'm quitting Grayson's."

Her mother shrugged her shoulders. "Your father and I said that you would never last. Linda, when are you going to settle down and see something through?"

Linda walked into her bedroom and closed the door. The new man, she supposed, was on his way to the airport, joking perhaps with the taxi driver. Soon he would be air-borne, traveling with the speed of sound and persistently smiling. How could such a superficial face conceal such despair? Linda threw herself on the bed and began to cry, uncertain what had provoked the tears, whether release from danger, the fate of the new man's son, or the new man himself.

# The Woman with the Hysterical Eyes

The woman had terrible brown eyes and a cream-white face. Someone said a tragedy had occurred in her life. Her child had been killed by a train, it was said, as she stood on the street only a few feet away. Kriel often thought it would be a wonderful face to paint if one could only somehow have the eyes boil on the canvas the way they did when seen. He knew, however, that he would never make the attempt as he would not think of intruding so cruelly into her life.

She sat on the west porch of the hotel which faced a soft pine forest. The trees on that side were so heavy nothing else could be seen up to the piece of gray or blue or white that happened to be the sky on that particular day. She was always in the same position, body straight up, head erect, with eyes looking off into the distance. Even when she read, which she sometimes did, her eyes seemed to penetrate the width of the book so that their energy flowed out its back and off into the silence.

Each morning when he went out into the hills to sketch he passed her, and she dampened his mood. He thought it wrong that at such a time she should be left alone. He decided she must be a widow. Her parents must be dead also. Friends, no doubt, had come to console her in the first frantic moments of grief but they had drifted off, pulled by the necessity of their own lives. Even when he was sketching she was apt to intrude into his work. He would wonder if she were still sitting there. When he returned in the evening his question would be answered. As he came striding down the path towards the porch he would catch a glimpse of her black dress and then her eyes staring beyond him to where the red sun was impaling itself on the evergreens.

After a while he almost felt he knew the woman, and passing her he had the desire to say something. Her silent hysteria fascinated him, terrified him as well. If there had been someone whom he knew who knew her he would have sought an introduction. But she was always alone. The other guests wove, interwove, fabrics of life were created, but she existed out of their pattern, not even part of the dining room surge. Several times at dinner he specifically looked for her, but she was not there. He decided she must have dinner in her room, and he imagined the scene with the table placed near the window and her staring out into the gathering darkness.

He didn't speak to her. The more he thought about it the more he drew back, sensing that perhaps his motives would be misunderstood and he would be regarded as having amorous intentions. He always kept his head straight to the front pretending he was not even conscious she was there.

She surely was not conscious of him. What did occupy her mind? He presumed it was that moment playing across her consciousness—the train looming at her with its hard steel face and she frozen in that instant of knowledge. Possibly there was guilt. She had permitted the child to walk too far from her. She had not called loudly enough for it to hear.

He tried to dismiss her from his mind and for several days took to circling the hotel and entering by the front entrance. He was ashamed of himself for this, knowing it was actually some sort of involvement which was responsible for his behavior. And at that he did not get her out of his mind. He was always conscious she was on the porch, sitting in her solitary grief.

Her name was Drummond, he discovered. His fascination went so far it dragged him against his will up to the desk clerk to make discreet inquiries. She came from

Boston. And that set his mind to imagining her milieu. He pictured a cultured, repressed world in which the agonies that boiled were always kept nicely under the surface until with volcanic strength they erupted into some fearful cataclysm.

One thing particularly had caught his fancy. He wished to see her walk. He had a vague feeling she was incapable of it, trauma having robbed her of the power. He thought of her being wheeled from her bedroom to the porch and back again, with the hours of silent gazing the only other fact in her life. But he knew this was ridiculous. If she had been an invalid in a wheel chair he would have known it. It was merely a manifestation of his curiosity taking a particular bizarre form.

Yet it would not leave him alone. One afternoon he lost interest in the cliff he was sketching, and he found himself, almost before he knew it, on his way back to the hotel. At this unusual hour would he trap her in some phase of her routine that was not known to him? When he came through the gate and saw her, eyes into a book, he was disappointed as if some play he was watching had not led up to the situation he had expected.

From then on he did it frequently, and then one afternoon his efforts were rewarded. He came up the path and she was not there. It excited him as at the end of a long search. But then he feared she might be in her room.

He began to hunt for her, at the same time smirking at himself, amazed he should be capable of such stupidity.

She was not in the bar. He studied all the faces. Not in the dining room. He walked through hurriedly. Not on the sun porch—only the flaccid, slovenly women lolling in the wicker chairs.

He walked out the back entrance of the hotel down the steps into the garden. There she was. She was walking along one of the paths, head slightly tilted down, gazing at the flowers. To him she seemed a dream-walker. No doubt the forms and colors of the buds were stamped on her retina but she was not viewing them. Her real self was within, gazing upon other screens which had their own stereotypes.

For a moment he loitered near her, pretending to study the flower beds. As usual he allowed words to form in his mind. It would be so simple really, stooping down to begin with a casual voice, "Aren't these roses magnificent?" And perhaps it was the very word she craved. It might break through to the ice caverns where she was, as a ray of sunlight pulling her back to the world where her salvation lay.

He could not bring himself to say it. Had she been a more vulgar woman it would have been simple. But she would perceive immediately that he was making conversation. In some sense he would be discovered, even though it was a falsehood, and his pride rebelled against it. She passed on and he made no effort to follow.

That evening he was amazed to see her enter the dining room escorted by a tall, blond-haired man. He had never seen him before, and he immediately surmised it was someone who had come to visit her. They sat at a nearby table and he studied them covertly. For some reason he came to the conclusion it was the woman's lawyer and they were discussing business. She sat staring at him and his hands moved, sharp gesticulations, pointing statements Kriel could not hear.

When they rose to leave Kriel did so too. He followed them as they passed out the main entrance of the hotel to the path which cut its way across the lawn. He pretended he was merely loitering in the evening, meanwhile adjusting his pace to theirs so that he was always only a few yards behind them. Such subterfuge he soon discovered was unnecessary, as they were so caught up in talk they were unconscious of anything else. Every now and then a phrase spoken a little louder than the rest floated back to him.

"Emily, come back."

He could not hear the answer.

". . . such foolishness. Why do you wish to tie a rope around your neck?"

He had the impression, although he could not see, that she was not looking at the speaker.

He heard a word from her, "I told you in the letter. . . ." The voice faded. It was a sweet, cultured voice but in its interior were nuances of passion.

Abruptly she stopped in the middle of the path. Her hands were clenched at her side and her words came as a shrill cry, "God! God! Gerald." Kriel froze. He had never heard such agony before. The woman's eyes had suddenly found speech.

For a long second she stood that way and then she turned. He caught a glimpse of her face as she passed him walking quickly towards the hotel. How long, he wondered, could she endure. Would she not pass over into madness as a salvation?

He followed them back into the hotel; but they had disappeared, and sitting at the bar, he attempted to unravel the events. Who was the blond-haired man? Her husband perhaps? Her brother? He was not, as he had first thought, her lawyer. But he could come to no conclusion. He had a few more drinks and then he went upstairs to bed.

When he awoke in the morning the notion was in his head that the woman had left. He hurried downstairs to see if his hunch was right, and, passing the empty chair, he felt relief. She had gone. The blond-haired man, whoever he was, had conquered.

He was happier that day. He sketched exuberantly with an irresponsibility that pleased him. And returning in the evening to find the chair still unoccupied he was sure. Now his fancy passed over to some young girls who were strutting about the porch in evening gowns. They were clear-eyed huntresses, nostrils distended, sniffing for game. Even he came within their orbit of inquiry. It rather amused him and he wondered if he should not permit himself to be ensnared.

Little knots of people were moving up and down the steps of the hotel—and suddenly she was there. She appeared wearing a coat on her shoulders, moving into the twilight like the somnambulist she was.

His breath caught. He had not wished her to stay. He had wanted her out of his life so that the fearful eyes would never trouble him again.

Resolutely he determined not to follow her. But the next night it was the same, and the night after that. She had merely changed her routine. Here too there was a pattern. She would be gone in the morning before he was up and would be back before he had returned.

Where did she go? he wondered. He had to follow. The evening his resolution was finally broken he waited for her on the porch. The black gown, the immaculately chiseled face appeared through the doorway, moved down the steps. She was at the end of the path before he set out after her.

She turned into the woods and he turned also. Now they were moving along a narrow, ill-defined trail. He could hear her moving ahead of him and so he did not have to keep her in sight.

The trail wound uphill. Occasionally he would catch a glimpse of her, hands in front of her face, pushing away the overhanging branches. Without any warning at all they broke into a clearing.

Here the path ended. They were on the top of a cliff, and on the other side of the clearing was a sharp drop. He stood under the protective canopy of the woods watching her breathlessly. With firm, slow steps as if she were a participant in some religious ritual she moved to the cliff's edge and stood looking down.

He could almost read her mind. She was deliberating. At the bottom of the cliff lay the peace she desired. With the hands of sharp rocks it was beckoning to her. And combatting it was only a habit of life, not even the fear of pain, tugging her back so that she appeared to be sway-ing, visibly pulled by the two forces.

He sweated, fearful that if he should make any sound it would send her hurtling down. Then after about half an hour when she finally turned he pulled back into the shadows to let her pass. He wished to return to his room, to smoke, to think. What must he do? Could he go blandly up to the hotel manager and announce his suspicions? Would he not seem absurd with only the walks that led past a cliff to back up his assertions? Would it not be said that he was the hysterical one contriving out of a set of tragic circumstances to build a fantastic myth?

But it was true. He was certain of it. Death was claiming the woman's mind; she was preparing herself. As a soldier about to go into battle studies scenes of carnage so that he will become accustomed to them, she was accommodating herself to the bitter-sweet draught of peace by sipping it morning and afternoon at the path's end.

He followed her back, and all night the thoughts rioted in his brain. He could not sleep. Now he took the manager's position. He pointed out to himself that he had always been very suggestible. He recalled childhood when too weird stories had sent him to bed in paroxysms of terror. He imagined going up to the woman and confronting her and the hysteria of her eyes acquiring a new hysteria of wonder as she tried to fathom this manner of man who was attributing such wild motives to her.

When morning came he descended haggard to breakfast and afterwards as he had known he would he took the trail that led to the cliff. She was already there—staring, staring. He noted now that her shoulders had a quiet resignation to them which almost sang of the peace she so ardently desired. Suppose then he should find the courage to come forth out of the copse and bare himself as a would-be savior, what new perception of the world could he offer which would make her revalue it?

Almost against his will he forced himself out into the clearing. The sound of his body brushing against the leaves brought her about facing him with her staring eyes.

He smiled at her, nodding his head, as a sign of good morning. Her lips opened and closed in a quiet answer.

"Good morning."

And the pitch of her voice was so natural it left him confused, incapable after his herculean effort of proceeding further. He passed on across the clearing as if their meeting had been the most casual of accidents.

His cowardice annoyed him. He upbraided himself for being a child unwilling to face an important unpleasantness. Analogous occasions on which he had behaved badly returned to him. But in those cases it had only been his own life that was at stake. Here a tea-table self-consciousness had become almost murder. He resolved that that afternoon he would see the thing through.

He ate lunch with a fierce determination and then with the same desperate intensity he walked up the path.

When he saw that the woman was not in her usual place he knew it was his intrusion of the morning which had altered matters. She had sought a more private spot in which to accomplish her destruction. Hysteria welled up within him. What if at this very moment it was occurring? He began to search frantically, moving out in ever-widening circles.

At last he saw her. She was at the bottom of the cliff moving as quickly as he was. He attempted to find a way down the cliff's surface but the grade was too steep. By the time he had made the necessary detours she was gone.

Was it possible she knew he suspected? It almost seemed that way. Now she had become cleverer. In the evening when he attempted to follow her, she eluded him. Perhaps it was only chance. The woods were dark and it was easy to go off on a tangent. But the following morning the same thing happened. They came to a fork in the trail and he would have sworn she had veered right, but following the trail deep into the woods he found he had lost her again.

It was not until the second evening after she had deserted her old haunts that he discovered the new one. He was surprised to find that all she had done was to move three or four hundred yards further along the edge of the cliff. If he had continued on from the old spot he would have run into it. She stood as he had seen her on the two

other occasions, staring down. But this time she was
dressed differently. She wore white instead of the cus-
tomary black. That was significant, he knew. His theory
was that she had put aside her mourning as a symbol of
its final termination. His heart leaped. Was it to be that
evening? It would be so much better if just as it were to
happen he were to reach out and grasp her. Then frus-
trated, emotion boiling within her, she would break. He
would not have to pry it out of her. She would cry on
his shoulder and the words would seethe out without
prompting.

She turned to go and he had still said nothing. A full
moon shone directly onto her face. He saw the face with
wonder. It was dead. The pain had been cancelled—from
the eyes also; it had died in anticipation. He wondered if
it was right for him to interfere, and by the time he had
debated the question she was gone.

Now he knew. She would come up the path in the
morning. She would move with slow, even steps to the
cliff's edge. She would not hesitate a moment. The steps
would take her over the brink and that last glimmer of
life which lingered in her limbs would be crushed from
her.

He had delayed so long. He had allowed her spirit to
perish. Perhaps if he now intruded he would be more
guilty than ever. But still it was necessary for him to act.

He would come here early. He would wait for her. He would prevent the final consummation.

Before retiring he left word with the room-clerk to be awakened at six-thirty. Dreams oppressed him. He was at the path's end and the pale, dead face was saying to him, "You let the nerve die. And now you will save the shell of the tooth." The telephone rang and he rejoiced to be awake again.

He dressed quickly, and omitting breakfast he hurried up the trail. Like a sentinel walking a post, he paced up and down the cliff's edge constantly turning to stare at the path and then constantly looking at his watch.

Eight-thirty. Nine. Nine-thirty. Ten. Was it possible, he wondered, the woman could have given him the slip again? He dared not leave the spot and yet he wished to hunt through the woods.

By twelve he knew she would not come. He had worked himself up into panic and he ran through the woods back to the hotel. Possibly her routine had again changed and he would find her as he had seen her first seated on the porch dressed in black.

In front of the hotel was a crowd. An ambulance was drawn up at the entrance. Hospital orderlies were lifting something into a stretcher. Although he knew what it was he had to ask.

One of the guests told him excitedly, "She jumped four stories just a few moments ago."

He couldn't listen further. He went to his room and sat in a chair. Now he knew the agony of the woman's soul intimately as if it had passed into him.

# In a Great Tradition

The name given to him was preposterous enough to affect his whole life—Roderick Armand Gallo. So perhaps it all began at the christening fount. When I met him, he was thirty-five years beyond that, and had already acquired a wife and two children, in addition to a prodigious notion of his importance as a painter. I came across him at the opening of an art show, his face ostentatiously turned away from the works of his competitor. Weren't these awful? he inquired, without bothering to find out what connection I had with the artist in question, and before I even had time to reply, he had managed to annihilate critically everything that was in the room. Form was nil and color was insipid. Even the quality of the paint used was not good. Since the creator of the show was neither my brother, nor my uncle, nor my cousin, I listened to the critique without a murmur. By this time I knew that artists rarely approved of each other, and the less well known were always more hostile than the famous. Armand's bile was particularly bitter, and so I came to the conclusion that he had no reputation at all.

Nor was I wrong. He had painted for fifteen years and had had only two small shows. The reputation he had was for confusion. Not only were his canvasses enormous swirls of paint, but his conversation partook of the same sticky quality. An hour and a half with Armand and one's head was whirling. The words he used were familiar enough, but somehow the sequence was disconnected from meaning. In the end one knew what one had known at the beginning—here was a passionate will that had been denied all intellectual equipment.

Certainly no one could deny Armand's passion. It appeared in every florid gesture he made. He was a handsome man, an olive-skinned Sicilian, and as he spoke, his body would accent the vibrato of his speech. Watching him, one felt one was viewing a dance—invective, joy, elegy, epic. If only one could have comprehended fully! But one could not. The children were the only things that he had produced that were clear and unambiguous. When I met them, I knew immediately that this was the sort of creation at which he excelled. That happened a week after I first saw him at the show.

He had taken down my name and telephone number and called to invite me to a party.

I was unaware at that time how little the clock meant to Armand, and so I did not make a prudent adjustment to allow for his foibles. He had said eight-thirty, and so I arrived at eight-thirty, and found the family still at dinner. Leda Gallo was tall, blond, and cool-looking. She appeared to have been clipped from the pages of a fashion magazine, and my first impression was that this had been a marriage of opposites, the south had wooed the north, the Latin and the Nordic had merged for mutual benefits. But ten minutes in that room convinced me of my error. She was really a female Armand. Both were storm and rain, whirlwind and tempest. And the children they had produced were infant cyclones.

Neither Armand nor Leda were the sort who concealed anything, and as the tempests to which they had given birth roared about the room, they explained that neither of them had wanted children. The children had just happened. They had taken precautions, but apparently no precautions could circumvent Armand's seed.

"I've been thinking of having an operation," Armand said. "We certainly can't afford to have another kid."

I could understand that well enough. Even two children in those quarters were an unbearable luxury.

The three small rooms were full, but not with furniture. Indeed there was a minimum of furniture to be seen. Children and paintings were the staples here. The children screamed and whistled and howled, and the paintings did likewise. I do not know how many paintings were there, but every bit of wall space was covered. And since Armand was particularly fond of vivid colors done on large expanses, one felt one was drowning in red and orange.

Armand went on explaining how such operations were done, and whatever he forgot to tell, Leda added. I don't know why this should have embarrassed me. If one wanted such an operation, I suppose there was no reason not to have one. And yet it didn't seem right that Armand should make himself sterile.

But I didn't argue about it. Other guests arrived and we left that subject.

It is difficult for me to say quite why I kept on seeing Armand. The most probable reason is that he wanted to see me. Every now and again, the doorbell of my apartment would ring, and I would open the door to find Armand come to discuss some intellectual problem. I have always been interested in philosophy, and he apparently considered me a sage. I was flattered, of course. He asked me about Plato and Kant and Lessing, and I briefed him as best I could. I knew even then that I was not helping him, only adding to his confusion. What difference did it make whether he could explain the categorical imperative or not? There were more significant imperatives in his life. The fact was he couldn't make a living. He had four mouths to feed, and he could scarcely feed himself. So he was always borrowing from me, and stealing art books, and doing occasional manual work, to keep all his responsibilities from starving. Once or twice I talked to him about this.

"Why don't you get a job?" I asked him. "This is no way to live."

"Sure, get a job. When would I paint?"

"Weekends," I answered.

He shook his head. "Never. That way you destroy yourself."

But one day he had to begin thinking of a job. Quite clearly he had not got an operation, and the exuberance of his being had once more overflowed. Yes, there was to be another child. He did not tell me; I saw the creature growing. At first I was not sure. I merely thought that Leda was putting on weight, and that this also accounted for the shortness of her temper. She was less affable than she had been. She was beginning to feel the years, I decided. Her looks were going and she was not reconciled to the downward march to middle-age. But the next time I saw her, I could not doubt. Once more the fortress had fallen and the irrational work of life was busy within her.

"We live like pigs," she said, apropos of nothing, "like pigs." And then she looked pugnaciously at Armand. "Well, Armand, don't you want to go and paint a picture?"

I attempted to change the subject, but she was only interested in attacking her husband.

"Hasn't Armand shown you his latest?" she inquired sharply. "It's not dry yet, so that's why it's not hung up. Go ahead, Armand. I'm sure he's dying to see it."

But no sooner had he decided to follow her suggestion, than she became wild. Always before, through all the hardships and disappointments, she had been on his side. He had said that he was another Kandinsky and she had agreed. He had complained about the cliques that prevented his work from being acknowledged, and she had become even more specific. But this, her third pregnancy, had converted her to the opposition. Armand was now living with his most savage critic. That day was the first time I saw him flee. At last, provoked into a rage, he got up and went out slamming the door behind him. Leda did not question which side I was on. It was inconceivable that I would think of defending Armand.

"He should be convinced by this time," she said. "All right, he's not a painter. I'm satisfied. Just let him be a man."

It was clear enough what she wanted him to do, and a few weeks later Armand gave in. He explained to me that he had been thinking things over and had come to the conclusion that he ought to get a job. As he sat in my apartment speaking in bold periods, my heart sank. What he was doing was, of course, the prudent thing, in fact the only possible thing. I had recommended this course years before. But nevertheless, it seemed wrong to me. Working was not his style of life. Indeed, what would he work at? What was his area of proficiency? I tried to imagine and I couldn't. I thought of Armand as a grocery clerk, as a telephone operator, as a secretary. No, none of these occupations was proper to the man. He had found his proper life—painting bad pictures and producing children. But unfortunately the two things he did best didn't go well together.

"Oh, you'll find something, I'm sure," I said, dissembling my feelings. "And it won't be bad at all. Once you get into the swing of things, you'll find plenty of time to go on painting."

"Sure, sure," he said, but I knew that he didn't believe me.

And at that moment, if I had been as wealthy as a foundation I would have endowed Armand. Everyone helped the talented, but were not the untalented entitled to something?

Armand left, and the next time I saw him, he was on a scaffolding fifteen feet above the street, clad in white overalls, painting a building. I shouted up to him. "Armand," and he waved back to me.

"Have a beer with me later," he said, and we made an appointment.

Ah, he had been tricking me. All these years he had had this profession. He had done it as a very young man. It had been the profession of his father. So what he was doing was really only accepting his heritage. He had mistaken what kind of a painter he was, but life had insisted on rectifying the error. Or, at least so I told myself, even though I was not quite happy with the way he spoke. Now, if anything, he had become more aesthetic than ever before. Things were coming clear to him. He had a new style in mind. True, he could not create as much, but what he did was better. I could feel his dissatisfaction boiling about me, and it made me uncomfortable.

Of course, when the baby was born, I went to visit Leda at the hospital. If it had occurred to me at times that this was a tragic occasion, my view changed as soon as I entered the room. The flowers I had sent smiled at me. Birth, they assured me, was always a good thing. Nor were they the only smiling presences. Leda looked as if the swan had just descended and she had been truly touched by divinity. It was a cute baby, she told me, a very cute baby, and Armand agreed. I saw then that he was actually proud of his creative capacities. Perhaps he actually conspired in his own ruin. At any rate, I could not believe that this was a man who would ever consent to have an operation. The child was the most beautiful he had yet produced, he informed me, and he rushed me off to have a look at it.

The minute creature slept unaware of praise or blame, and I made the appropriate remarks. Did it look like Armand? I do not know. I said that it did. He contradicted me and swore that the resemblance to Leda was unmistakable. And then suddenly it awoke and began to rage. The small hands scratched frantically at the face. I could feel its irrational insistence pushing out beyond the glass. It had demanded to be born, and its birth meant changes.

Yes, great changes.

"We shall have to move," Armand told me. "Of course we can't live where we are any longer. I've found a place in the suburbs. It isn't very convenient, but it's nice. Six rooms," he went on, "you'll like it when you see it. Leda's very pleased. She's always wanted to live in the country."

I would visit him, I assured him. Of course, I would.

Cross my heart. But I must admit that I never did see the garden apartment in which he lived. Every now and again, he would meet me on the street and ask, "When are you coming out?" "Soon," I would answer. But it became apparent that soon was the equivalent of never. I planned to go, but I just didn't get around to it. Perhaps the confusion of Armand trying to explain the route that you took was too much. I did not go, but others did. They came back with the report that it was a very handsome place. Not only were there six rooms and two baths, but nearby there was a playground for the children. Unfortunately the children did not use the playground, although it was splendidly equipped. For some reason or other, they preferred the house, and despite the spaciousness of things, there was an implausibility to the existence that Leda and Armand led. Television was on in every room, and though Armand still spoke about his paintings, my informants were unclear about where this painting was done. In fact, as far as they could see, there was no studio, and what was more, no paintings. Unlike the previous apartment, this one had been kept with walls bare. Indeed, this was the most difficult thing for me to believe—not one of Armand's paintings was up.

And then came the final catastrophic news some eight months later—Leda was pregnant again.

I remember how stunned I was when I heard this. I

had not seen Armand for three months, and I had assumed that things were going well. But the brazenness of this fourth pregnancy outraged me. Armand, I concluded was incorrigible. No matter how potent his being, surely some controls should have availed.

"She must get an abortion," I told my informant. "I don't give a damn about the morality. Armand must think of himself."

"What do you care?" my friend asked me. "Why are you getting so angry about it?"

I suppose it was instinct. Something told me that Armand couldn't stand this last blow.

But apparently I was wrong. For the next time that I ran into him, he appeared to be more exuberant than ever. His fourth child, a sweet little daughter, had come into the world and was the most beautiful of all. What was even better, perhaps, was that he was painting again. He was using the studio of a friend of his; and a few nights a week before catching the train home, he went up there and worked for an hour or so. As always, he had some important new ideas. Would I come around and look at his things some evening? In any case, he wanted to talk to me. Fine, fine, I said, I would be happy to.

"How about Tuesday?" he asked. And he wrote out the address for me. I felt I had been neglecting him and I determined to keep my word.

183

Inevitably the studio was in a run-down loft, and equally inevitably six flights up. I stumbled up the stairs, periodically pausing to catch my breath. At last, I came to the floor with the large pencilled sign, "Prior" on it, the name of Armand's friend. I knocked on the door, and Armand threw it open.

"Come in, come in," he said, obviously delighted to see me.

"It's quite a climb," I said. And then I was silent. I had caught sight of the paintings. They were massive, larger than ever, and as always, orange, red, yellow, green. But no longer was Armand an abstractionist. Now he was in love with vegetation. I don't know whether these were the plants of imagination, or the plants of reality, so badly were they drawn, and so ill-equipped was I to name them. But somehow they had managed to come alive. The green, presumably grass, seethed like worms. The insane corollas appeared on the point of becoming foetuses. I felt that I was at the heart of birth, and that all this life was intent on choking me.

"Different, aren't they?"

"Yes," I gasped, still unable to get my reason operating. And so busy was I trying to comprehend and then fight off the pictures that for some time I did not notice that we were not alone. A third had entered the room. But when I heard a voice calling out, "Armand," I turned.

Yes, there was a woman there, and only then did I realize that Armand's friend was his mistress.

"This is Gloria," Armand said.

"Aren't they marvelous?" Gloria asked. But I was scarcely listening. I could not take my eyes off the woman's middle. She was so obviously pregnant.

It is now clear to me that all of this was predictable. A suburb was no place for Armand. House painting was not his true vocation. The children he had had by Leda had driven him out of the house, and he had come upon Gloria. The affair had been going on for some time, but now Leda would have to know.

"We're going to Mexico," Gloria said. "Armand is in his most creative period. He has to have the chance to paint."

She had certainly used the proper word. It stirred my fancy. Could this stocky Sicilian possibly be the embodiment of the fertility principle, irrational Pan, illicit Priapus, come to live among us? I recalled that such gods were finally torn asunder by their women worshippers. No wonder. How many children would Gloria bear him? And then who would be next?

Yes, Mexico was necessary, Armand agreed. "It's the only way out. It'll be tough on Leda. But what are you going to do?"

Exactly, what were you going to do? Armand was Armand, and I wasn't sure whether the world was right for him or wrong. I listened sympathetically, but I didn't know what to suggest.

# An Appointment with the Master

SCENE: *Miss Prescott's office in the Prescott Employment Agency. The most important element in the set is Miss Prescott's elegant modern desk at which the owner of the agency is seated as the curtain rises. Upstage is a door on the glass of which can be seen the name* RUTH PRESCOTT, *painted, of course, on the outside of the glass, the letters shining through. Stage left is a window. On Miss Prescott's desk are a battery of telephones.*

*Miss Prescott is a modish woman of forty-five, alert, efficient, tailored. She is at the moment busy on one of the phones.*

MISS PRESCOTT: Yes, this is Miss Prescott speaking . . . No, Mr. Dodds, nothing yet . . . I know, Mr. Dodds; we're working on it. The important thing is not to get discouraged, Mr. Dodds. Your mental outlook is every-thing . . . Nice talking to you, Mr. Dodds. 'Bye. We'll be in touch with you as soon as anything turns up. *(She hangs up. Drums her fingers on the desk nervously for a moment, and starts to get up from the desk when the telephone rings again. She answers, standing.)* Hello, Miss Prescott speaking. . . . I'm very happy for you, Mr. Ryan. I know the client was delighted with you . . . It's a sound corporation. Great possibilities for advancement . . . No, the check is not made out to me personally; it's the Prescott Employment Agency . . . 'Bye, Mr. Ryan, it was nice serving you. *(She hangs up, and walks to the window as the clock on her desk chimes.)* Damned chimes. I need a silent clock. Four o'clock. God the day's almost over. I've only smoked four cigarettes today and I haven't had a cocktail. That will please the doctor. But what nasty dreams I had last night. I must remember them for my appointment tomorrow. I wonder if I will ever be well. Lord, I must smoke. *(She rushes back to the telephones and picks one up.)* Elena, send down for a package of cigarettes . . . That's my business. I'll smoke if I want to. *(There is a knock on the door. She hangs up the phone.)* Come in. *(A middle-aged Hindu of about fifty enters. He is dressed in traditional Indian clothes, and seems quite out of place in these very modish, western surroundings. He, himself, seems conscious of this, and lingers nervously at the door. Miss Prescott eyes him suspiciously.*) Yes?

RAMANANDA: Miss Prescott?

MISS PRESCOTT: Yes.

RAMANANDA: You were expecting me, weren't you? I'm Swami Ramananda.
[*Miss Prescott is not sure whether she was expecting him or not. She checks quickly with her appointment book.*]

MISS PRESCOTT: Oh yes, your name is down on my appointment book. Do come in, Swami.

RAMANANDA: Your secretary said it was quite all right to come straight in.

MISS PRESCOTT: Naturally. It was just that my mind was elsewhere. Won't you sit down, Swami? Would you repeat your last name for me?

RAMANANDA: Ramananda.

MISS PRESCOTT: *(With visible pleasure)* Swami Ramananda. I say it correctly, don't I?

RAMANANDA: Quite correctly.

MISS PRESCOTT: *(Her gracious best)* Now, how can I be of service to you, Swami?

RAMANANDA: It's quite simple, Miss Prescott. I'm looking for a job.

MISS PRESCOTT: *(Taken aback)* A job?

RAMANANDA: Exactly. Don't let these clothes put you off. I am leaving my order. I am becoming westernized. *(Miss Prescott is more surprised than ever.)* I see that startles you. A month ago I myself would have thought it inconceivable. But that is my decision. I have had enough of contemplation.

MISS PRESCOTT: What kind of a job did you have in mind, Swami?

RAMANANDA: Please let us forget that title. From now on I am Mr. Gosh. What do you think I could do? I thought you might have some suggestions.

MISS PRESCOTT: I'm not sure. I must have your background.

RAMANANDA: Very impractical! Offhand it would seem to dictate my being a teacher. I could, of course, give lessons in Sanskrit or lecture on Hindu philosophy or art. But I want nothing like that. Nor do I wish to be an interpreter at the UN. You must understand I have had an experience in reverse. When I was young, a voice told me I must desert the world and commune with the Absolute. It was only a small whisper and perhaps I should not have listened. Now I am fifty years old and the self-same voice is shouting at me that I have been a fool, that there is no Absolute, that there is only this. You agree don't you, Miss Prescott?

MISS PRESCOTT: To tell you the truth, Swami . . . I'm sorry, Mr. Gosh, India has always fascinated me.

RAMANANDA: You have been there?

MISS PRESCOTT: No, I have only seen travelogues.

RAMANANDA: Nevertheless, I am happy you think well of us. Perhaps some day you will actually go.
   [*Elena, a platinum blond of thirty with evocative*

*hips enters, with a package of cigarettes. She hands them to Miss Prescott.*]

MISS PRESCOTT: Thank you, Elena. *(She opens the package and takes out a cigarette.)*

RAMANANDA: Would you forgive me, if I took one? I have never smoked.

MISS PRESCOTT: Of course, of course. *(She walks to him.)* Here, let me light it for you.

RAMANANDA: *(Puffing)* Delicious. It's very bad for you, I understand.

MISS PRESCOTT: I'm trying to give it up.

RAMANANDA: Why?

MISS PRESCOTT: It's such a senseless habit. Why commit suicide?

RAMANANDA: Ah, you want to live. That is admirable. I can see that you will be of great help to me.

MISS PRESCOTT: *(Laughs nervously)* I? Mr. Gosh, you're wrong. I can confess it to you, a holy man . . .

RAMANANDA: *(Holding up his hands)* No, no!

MISS PRESCOTT: Well, someone who has been a holy man —my life is a mess. I go through this routine every day— to work and home again—and I don't have the slightest notion why I do it. I'm in the hands of two doctors. That's how serious my situation is. You've come to the wrong place if you want advice. *(The telephone rings.)* Excuse me please. The phone never stops ringing. *(She runs to the phone.)* No, Elena, I can't talk to Mr. Dodds again. He's too old. Who can find a sixty-year-old man a job? . . . And don't forward any other calls. I'm in conference with Mr. Gosh.

RAMANANDA: My cause is perhaps hopeless. You recall I am fifty.

MISS PRESCOTT: We'll find you something, I'm sure. Your case interests me. But I am not certain that you are not making a mistake, Swami.

RAMANANDA: No, I have lost my vision.

MISS PRESCOTT: But you had it once.

RAMANANDA: Perhaps! Perhaps!

MISS PRESCOTT: I have never had anything even like a vision.

RAMANANDA: Really? Never?

MISS PRESCOTT: No, never. It seems to me that my life has been mainly answering telephone calls.

RAMANANDA: You're unmarried, I take it.

MISS PRESCOTT: I've been divorced twice.

RAMANANDA: Any children?

MISS PRESCOTT: A daughter at college who scarcely ever writes.

RAMANANDA: Ah, you're lonely.

MISS PRESCOTT: No, it's worse than that.

RAMANANDA: How strange. I have descended from the top of the mountain and I find the world beautiful.

MISS PRESCOTT: This beautiful? Swami, you are fifty years old, but you are a child. This is hell. Look out at the street. It's filthy. Worse than that, it's arid. This is a stone torture chamber in which we all wander about looking for something that we can't find.

RAMANANDA: How vehement you are! I found the street charming. A little too much traffic perhaps. But you can't have everything.

MISS PRESCOTT: Swami, I want God. Tell me how I can find God.

RAMANANDA: I don't know. I'm not even sure there is one. Remember, I've come to you for a job.

MISS PRESCOTT: You do know. You've seen him.

RAMANANDA: I? Well, perhaps I dreamed I did. But I can't show you a lost dream.
[*The telephone rings.*]

MISS PRESCOTT: I told that stupid girl not to disturb me.

195

*(She goes and picks up the phone.)* Miss Prescott speaking . . . How dare you, Mr. Dodds. You are not to use my private line. We spoke only a few minutes ago, and I told you I would let you know when I had anything. Now good-bye. *(She hangs up.)* Carrion!

RAMANANDA: You are sick, Miss Prescott.

MISS PRESCOTT: Yes, I am sick. You see how sick I am, Swami. *(She throws her head down on the desk.)*

RAMANANDA: *(Walks over to her)* What is it you fear, Miss Prescott? Death?

MISS PRESCOTT: I dread it.

RAMANANDA: The darkness?

MISS PRESCOTT: I do not want to be extinguished.

RAMANANDA: But you are still in the world.

MISS PRESCOTT: I loathe it.

RAMANANDA: You really are difficult to please.

MISS PRESCOTT: Swami, you have no right to leave your vocation. You must contact the divine again.

RAMANANDA: Perhaps I have come to the wrong employment agency.
[*Swami Ramananda starts toward the door, but Miss Prescott rushes over and bars his passage.*]

MISS PRESCOTT: No, I will not let you leave. I'm not the only one. Elena needs you, and so does my office manager Mr. Harding.

RAMANANDA: I told you I have resigned my calling.

MISS PRESCOTT: No, no. *(Calls out)* Elena! Bill!

RAMANANDA: Don't you see, I can do nothing for you? Even if I were still a swami, you would have to cooperate. You cannot see with my eyes.
[*Elena and Bill Harding enter. Harding is about forty, a good looking gray flannel type.*]

HARDING: What is it, Ruth?

MISS PRESCOTT: Do you see that man over there? That is Swami Ramananda.

HARDING: I'm very happy to make your acquaintance, sir.

MISS PRESCOTT: But he has decided to leave off being a swami and become merely Mr. Gosh.

HARDING: Well, that would seem to be his privilege.

MISS PRESCOTT: He's making a fool of himself. He wants to become like us.

HARDING: Again, I would say that that is his privilege.

MISS PRESCOTT: Bill, can you honestly say that you're happy?

HARDING: Swami, she's been very upset these last few days. You must forgive her.

RAMANANDA: Perhaps, then, you could take care of me, Mr. Harding. What I am looking for is a job. And please remember my name is Mr. Gosh.

HARDING: Exactly, Mr. Gosh! Now, Ruth, let me take Mr. Gosh into my office and I'll fill out a card.

MISS PRESCOTT: No, it's all right, Bill. I'm sorry. You can do it here. Elena, get a card from my desk.

[*Elena goes to the desk and takes a card out of one of the drawers. She hands it to Harding.*]

HARDING: Sit down, Mr. Gosh. The whole thing won't take a minute.

RAMANANDA: *(Sitting)* Thank you. Thank you.

HARDING: How old are you?

RAMANANDA: I was just fifty last Thursday.

HARDING: *(Writing)* Fifty years old. And what experience have you had?

RAMANANDA: Well, all that I've ever really been is a swami.

HARDING: From the job point of view I suppose we would have to say that that was no experience.

RAMANANDA: That's exactly what I told Miss Prescott.

HARDING: And what languages do you speak? English well, I can see.

RAMANANDA: About twenty-two dialects, not including Sanskrit.

MISS PRESCOTT: He doesn't want to be an interpreter at the UN, Bill.

HARDING: I see you have read my mind. That did seem like a promising possibility. Why, may I ask, do you object to interpreting?

RAMANANDA: Miss Prescott thinks I am mad. But I am in love with the world, and I don't want to be stuck off in some official corner of it.

HARDING: Where would you like to be?

RAMANANDA: As I go around the city, I see hundreds of little stores. It would be pleasant to be in one of them. They are really so very handsome and well lit. I'm sure I would enjoy working in such a pleasant prospect.

ELENA: Mr. Gosh, you have no experience. I spent five years in one. It would be no job for you.

MISS PRESCOTT: I told you that he was mad, Bill.

HARDING: I like you, Mr. Gosh. I like your point of view, and so I want to level with you. A job in one of those stores is not for a person of your quality. It's difficult work and not too remunerative.

RAMANANDA: If you say so. But I do not know quite what quality I am. And since I am not married, my demands are not great.

HARDING: There is very little future in clerking. I assume that you don't have the capital to undertake a venture of your own.

RAMANANDA: No. No capital. But I was not looking to the future. A job that I would really like, but I realize that I am too old for, would be as a fire fighter. It is really such an active life and I have never been quite active enough.

HARDING: *(Quickly)* Yes, you are too old for that. And I believe that you have to be a citizen. Your'e not a citizen, are you?

RAMANANDA: No, I'm not.

201

HARDING: Have you thought of insurance? There must be an Indian colony in the city, and you could sell them life insurance. It might be quite lucrative.

RAMANANDA: Don't you have any other ideas?

HARDING: You don't find that very appealing?

RAMANANDA: It's too much like what I have just been doing. That, of course, was insurance of a different sort. But I have a feeling that I should always be talking about death. My interest now is just the opposite. Do you understand, Mr. Harding?

HARDING: I'm trying to.

RAMANANDA: Now a post in a travel agency would be nice, among all those posters. I'm sure that the colors would cheer you up. And then there would always be happy people bustling in going away on a good time. I think I should soon become as frivolous as they are.

HARDING: Are you making fun of us?

ELENA: He is making fun of us, Bill.

RAMANANDA: Why do you say that?

HARDING: You're not the sort of man who's in favor of frivolity.

RAMANANDA: But I am, I assure you.

MISS PRESCOTT: Now I understand, Bill. He's come to test us.

RAMANANDA: Test you? Why should I want to test you?

MISS PRESCOTT: He's been sent to show us the frivolousness of our lives. *(Kneeling)* Master, I acknowledge you.

RAMANANDA: My dear woman, get up. I am not your master. I am not even sure that I am my own. And in addition, the one thing I don't find in any of your lives is frivolity.

MISS PRESCOTT: *(Who is etherealized)* He scourges us with his words, but it is in love.

HARDING: *(Trying to pull her up)* Ruth, get up, you are making a spectacle of yourself. Help me, Elena.

203

MISS PRESCOTT: You should be making a spectacle of yourself too, Bill Harding. What is your life worth?

HARDING: My life is my life, and I can take care of it.

MISS PRESCOTT: Swami, it is the most dreadful life—married to a woman who despises him—living beyond his means to please her—killing himself for nothing at all.

HARDING: I'm quitting, Ruth. How can you say such things before a stranger?

MISS PRESCOTT: Quit! Quit!

ELENA: Miss Prescott, control yourself.

MISS PRESCOTT: *(Turning on Elena)* And you're another one. Working here by day so that you can fornicate at night. I know that loveless heart of yours, Elena. One just like it has beat in my bosom for forty-five years. Oh, God, God, we must be whole again.

ELENA: *(Suddenly impressed)* Miss Prescott, is he really something?

MISS PRESCOTT: You have heard him speak? How can you doubt?

RAMANANDA: In India we are not so emotional. It will take me some time to get accustomed to the West.

ELENA: (*Approaching him diffidently*) You are wise, are you not, sir?

RAMANANDA: Those are your words, child, not mine. You will recall that I only came here in search of employment.

ELENA: What she said of me is true. I have been little better than a whore. Am I forgiven? (*Ramananda turns away embarrassed.*) You reject me then?

RAMANANDA: No, no.

ELENA: I am forgiven.

RAMANANDA: Yes, you are forgiven.
[*Harding has been watching the conversion of Elena with amazement and scorn, and now he cannot stand it any longer. He thrusts himself between Elena and Ramananda.*]

HARDING: What have you done to these women? You have made them mad? How dare you come and upset them so?

RAMANANDA: Forgive me, I said nothing. It is all their doing.

HARDING: No, of course you said nothing. You're a really sly one. All that you did was ridicule everything that we believe in.

RAMANANDA: I have ridiculed nothing. You have been the ridiculers. All I asked to do was to participate in your society.

HARDING: With a sneer on your face.

RAMANANDA: Believe me, sir, if I have smiled it was not in contempt.

HARDING: You see what you have accomplished. You have destroyed this organization.

RAMANANDA: If I have done injury, it was unintentional and I kneel and beg forgiveness. (*He starts to kneel, but Elena interposes.*)

206

ELENA: Swami, restrain yourself. Don't kneel to that scum.

HARDING: You little bitch. I should kick in your teeth.

ELENA: Kick, Mr. Harding, kick. It will be the most virile thing you've ever done.
[*Harding makes a lunge at Elena and Ramananda holds him back.*]

RAMANANDA: Please, Mr. Harding. All this quarreling and for what?

HARDING: Yes, for what? A man wastes his life. He tries to do his best. But he ends up mingling with dirt. You asked the question—for what? Well, if you're so smart, Swami, give us the answer.

RAMANANDA: Inadvertently I've caused too much trouble already. I really must be going.

HARDING: Sure, now when we got down to essentials, you think you better leave. When the going's easy, you preen like a peacock, and all the hens come running.

MISS PRESCOTT: *(To Harding)* Now you get out of here. You've quit and in addition you're fired.

HARDING: Ruth, how can you talk this way? Don't you see what this man is doing to you?

MISS PRESCOTT: What's he doing?

HARDING: It's hocus-pocus, Ruth. It's the mysticism of the East. Can't you see the fellow's a phony.

RAMANANDA: You're right, Mr. Harding. I am an impostor.

ELENA: No, no.

RAMANANDA: Elena, Mr. Harding is the voice of reason. His skeptical eyes have seen through me. My intent in coming here was to ridicule you. I have always loathed the restless, nervous West, and on every possible occasion I spit in Westerners' eyes.

MISS PRESCOTT: It is what we deserve, Swami.

RAMANANDA: No, you deserve worse. The fact is I can't even bear being in the same room with you. And so I shall say good day.
   [*He turns to go, but Harding grasps him by the throat.*]

HARDING: Oh, no you don't, now you've got to tell us. You're a swami; you're supposed to help. What's wrong with us? Tell us. We can't go on living the way we have.

RAMANANDA: Well, if you don't like it, why not change?

HARDING: *(Suddenly getting the vision)* Yes, change. Why not change?

MISS PRESCOTT: That's exactly it, Bill. We've got to change.

ELENA: But what shall we change to, Master?

RAMANANDA: You take my job and I'll take yours. You can't go on doing the same thing forever.

MISS PRESCOTT: It's a parable, Elena. You have to understand what he is saying.

RAMANANDA: Miss Prescott is right and she will explain later. *(He takes out his wallet.)* I believe that there is a ten-dollar fee for processing my application. Is that correct?

HARDING: Yes, the fee is ten dollars.

RAMANANDA: You will notify me if anything appropriate comes up?

MISS PRESCOTT: Master, don't leave us.

ELENA: Stay with us, Master.

RAMANANDA: My telephone number is on the card. I can be reached easily. Remember it doesn't matter to me whether it's an indoor or outdoor job, and the salary isn't too important as long as you can live on it. *(He walks to the desk where the cigarettes are lying.)* Do you mind, Miss Prescott, if I take another cigarette? *(He takes one.)* You assure me that I have taught you something . . . *(He lights the cigarette.)* And you have taught me something as well. *(He exits smoking.)*

CURTAIN

# The New Kitsch

The dangers inherent in writing for a small, carefully selected group have long been well known. Coterie art tends to become effete and precious. The writer and his following are perhaps too finely adjusted to each other. Proper criticism becomes impossible. Moreover, in a small circle power can be more easily manipulated than in a large one. At the present time one can be least secure about the reputations in those arts in which the public has the least interest. Poetry is a perfect example of an art, deserted by the public, in which the reputation of the various practitioners often has little relationship to the quality of their work.

Until recently the novelist was much better off in this respect than the poet. Since there was great interest in the form in which he worked, the novelist could expect his novels to be discussed by many people. Most of these individuals, he knew, would be neither automatic supporters nor detractors, but impartial readers who would either praise his books because they found them interesting or dismiss them for being dull. This healthy situation disappeared with the rise of the avant-garde novel.

Avant-gardism has always had as one of its principal ingredients an enormous faith in the religion of art. So that from the first, avant-garde writers had a tendency to make art itself their subject matter. Another element inherent in avant-gardism was its bitter isolationism. The writers and artists conceived of themselves as fundamentally hostile to their society. When this antagonism led to social criticism, their work was often vivacious and interesting. But when it led them into absolute subjectivity and narcissism, their art became misty and vague. Avant-gardism also insisted that the artist be perpetually adventurous in his dealing with form. Experiment, once begun, never ceased and for many artists became the meaning of the entire creative act.

By the time that *Finnegans Wake* was published, it was obvious that the novelist must lose his broad audience, if he attempted to continue in the direction he was going. Whatever the merits of Joyce's work, it was preposterous to expect that many people would submit to its demands.

The Thirties with their interest in political matters interfered with the advance of avant-gardism. But with the end of the war, avant-gardism again became the principal influence on the talented young of America. Joyce, Kafka, James, Gide, and Faulkner were the gods of the intellectuals.

Such exotic masters, brilliant though they were, could not help but produce a strange assortment of disciples. The American novelist came to believe that no story could be told directly, that all diction must be fantastic and dazzling, that only a very few problems were interesting and that he himself was the most interesting problem of all. Some good books were written and many bad ones, but whether good or bad, almost all were determinedly eccentric. At this point the audience got up and began to leave, much to the chagrin of the novelist who immediately pointed out how dumb Americans are. It has always been the contention of advanced writers that when they speak people should snap to attention and listen.

I suppose it was the romantics who first confused the responsibilities of author and public. The genius was there to be admired and if he wasn't, there was something wrong with the world. But when put in different terms, one can see immediately how ridiculous the notion is. An entertainer who merely confuses and bores can hardly expect to receive applause. Serious novelists, I am aware, don't want to be thought of as entertainers. But they will either amuse their patrons or be dismissed. After all, if King Lear's jester hadn't been funny, he would not have been allowed to deliver all those wise remarks.

It is the natural function of art to be interesting. Neither the plays of the Greeks nor those of Shakespeare are boring. The novels of Dostoevsky and Tolstoy engage the reader at every moment. The problem with most coterie art is that it is dull. Too often it is also vacant. The artist is so puffed up with himself that he has no time for the business in hand. He postures and simpers and can't stop talking about himself. Finally, he finds himself alone and unappreciated.

The Germans have a splendid word for empty, spurious art. They call it *kitsch*. In our society this expressive term has in the main been used by the coteries to discredit what they call middle-class art. They have even developed theories to explain why *kitsch* is so prevalent in the modern world. America, we are told, being a mass society is in love with mass art which is a mass-produced product sold to the public by cynical manipulators. True art goes a-begging and is only admired by small elites.

But forty years ago, the novel was very alive in this country. I can remember the books that my mother, not a particularly literary woman, used to read and discuss with her friends. Galsworthy, Bennett, Willa Cather, Wells, E. M. Forster, were all read by these women. They were not deeply perceptive critics nor was there any need that they should be. It is not even desirable that an audience be composed of nothing but experts. But, though not critics, neither were these people mass-consumers. Nor are their children. That they have rejected the art novel does not necessarily mean that they have no taste. They may be even more alert than the avant-gardists themselves. There is a certain kind of *kitsch* that an intelligent observer recognizes immediately. For example, no self-respecting audience will accept those dull monstrosities that are called poetic plays. Five or six speeches and the audience is asleep. Only those who have systematically conditioned themselves to the absurd are able to stay awake. The intelligent reading public has given up serious novels because it has been disappointed too often. The pseudo-masterpieces, the overpraised works of highly derivative and pretentious authors, have destroyed its confidence in any criticism.

But the intelligent reading public has not given up reading. Disillusioned with coterie art and *kitsch* in general, it has gone elsewhere. Now the mature reader buys non-fiction in increasing quantities. He knows that American biographers and historians still write with great skill and clarity. Since these people have not as yet been told that they are artists, they do their jobs as best they can and collect their royalties when their books are successful.

It seems to me that the novel can still be saved if the novelists want to save it. To do so, however, will require a certain humility upon the part of the writer. The first thing he must do is to acquire respect for his audience. He is not there to either insult or teach them. His task is to present them with a novel. If the audience as a whole rejects his work, he must re-examine what he is doing. I do not mean that he must write down or pander to them. The really great artists of the past were always able to adapt themselves to their audiences and create their masterpieces within the limitations set by the times. If the American novelist is unwilling to make these concessions, he will finally become nothing but a coterie figure.

# Isaac Bashevis Singer

I should like to speak to you this afternoon about the great Yiddish writer, Isaac Bashevis Singer. Since I am Singer's editor, this may seem like special pleading, but I want to assure you that it is not. There are writers one publishes because one must, and others like Singer whom one offers to the public out of love and admiration.

For a good many of you, I suspect, this is the first time you have heard of Singer. Nor is this surprising, although Singer's short works have appeared in many notable magazines, and a collection of his stories and three novels have been published in book form. But in this era of busy presses and screaming publicity, it is easy for even an exceptional writer to be overlooked. This is particularly so when an author works in a so-called "minor" language and depends upon translation to be read at all. Scarcely anyone speaks Yiddish. The creation of the state of Israel and the resurrection of Hebrew as a spoken tongue has meant the death of Yiddish. At first sight it would appear that this is not a matter of any importance. Is it really possible that anything notable has been said in this "patois" that has not been said better in English, French, German, or Russian?

Well, it just happens that there is. Yiddish, as a literary language, has had only a brief history, but it already has its classics. There are, for example, the stories of Sholom Aleichem and Peretz which are quite unlike anything in any other tradition. I can remember how surprised I was when I first picked up *A Treasury of Yiddish Literature* to discover what riches were hidden in this obscure tongue.

The moment for Yiddish has passed and yet works of genius are still produced in it. Recently in *The Hudson Review* Vivian Mercier reviewed *The Magician of Lublin*, the third of the Singer novels to be translated into English. "From a dying language and a dying cultural tradition," Mercier wrote, "has sprung a living talent, as vivid and fresh as that of Chagall in painting a generation before. The moral for literature is that no language and no cultural tradition should be allowed to die if it can possibly be preserved; while a tradition lives at all it is always capable of new growth."

I concur most heartily. One of the sad things about

the current internationalism is that it is hostile by its very nature to minority cultures. It suppresses them through a kind of seduction. This, I know, cannot be prevented. The world marches on. One cannot afford romantic nostalgia. And at any rate, just before the moment of complete synthesis, comes an instant of grandeur when the aesthetic eye, constantly restless and constantly roving, seeks to traverse and comprehend the whole continuum of art. We are living, I believe, at such a moment. In fact, we are overwhelmed by it. The wealth of five continents is being offered to us. We should enjoy it while we may. The moment of brilliant, clashing cultures will pass, and we will have something else which may be very much less interesting.

And so I offer to you Isaac Bashevis Singer, a man who was born in Poland, whose youth was spent in the Warsaw Ghetto, and whose genius has flowered in America, in an alien country among a strange people speaking a foreign tongue. Indeed, Singer's life is itself a parable in which there is not one but many meanings.

I should make one thing clear at the outset: Singer, although a religious man, is not an Orthodox Jew. Jewish traditions play a great part in his stories, but he, himself, resists any dogma. Indeed the position of dogma in his stories is somewhat ambiguous. Dogma would seem to have its place in the community when it leads to true religious feeling. But as he writes in his novel *The Magician of Lublin:* "God exists. But all those who speak his name are liars."

That Singer should rely so heavily on Jewish tradition and folklore is in a sense not surprising. His father was a rabbi, and so as a child he was thoroughly trained in the traditions of his people. But we can see, from the fact that his older brother I. J. Singer, the author of the famous chronicle novel *The Brothers Ashkenazi,* moved in an entirely different direction from Bashevis, that the response to an environment is not automatic. I. J. Singer wrote in the rationalistic tradition; Bashevis Singer's art is a strange mixture of mysticism and skepticism.

One of the ironies in this "mystic's" life is that he has earned his living as a reporter for *The Jewish Forward,* a newspaper founded by socialists. Here his works are published in the original Yiddish, although thematically they are in direct opposition to the secular optimistic point of view of socialism. It is true, of course, that the socialism of the *Forward* is about as real as the opinions of John F. Kennedy, but, nevertheless, Singer is very far from being of the usual liberal persuasion. However, as both the Bible and Singer say, "God works in a mysterious way." The readers of the paper are delighted with his stories, although at times they suspect it is the devil who is speaking to them.

In fact, a certain segment of Singer's audience (in English as well as in Yiddish) is attracted to his books by his apparent diabolism. Some of these are of the devil's party and claim that Singer is on their side. There is a superficial justice to their view. Not only does the devil often appear in Singer's works, but very often he comes out the winner. Incidentally Singer's devil is not the tiresome old Nick of Stephen Vincent Benét but is much more closely allied to the Satan of *Paradise Lost*. The devil is primal evil, and a reality for Singer, not a figure in a pageant. In Singer's world good wrestles with evil and is the apparent loser. But where the diabolist misses the point is that Singer does not approve of negativity. He is an intransigent moralist—which I should add is not the same as being moralistic.

We can see by this, then, that Singer is not a man of the Enlightenment. As Irving Howe has written in *Commentary:* "Singer is related to the Jewish tradition not only in the obvious sense that he enjoys a close knowledge of the Jewish past. Most importantly, he is one of the few Yiddish writers whose relation to the Jewish past does not depend on that body of attitudes and values which we call Yiddishism. He writes *in* Yiddish, but is often quite apart from the Yiddish tradition. He is, so to say, a writer of the pre-Enlightenment and post-Enlightenment; he would be equally at home with a congregation of medieval Jews and a gathering of modern intellectuals, perhaps more so than at a meeting of the Yiddish PEN club; he has a strong sense of the mystical and antique, but also a stern awareness of psychoanalytic disenchantment; he has evaded both the religious pieties and the rationalism of nineteenth century East European Judaism."

With most of this I agree, but I must make one important qualification. Singer is at home with modern intellectuals, but he does not share many of the fashionable views on literature held by intellectuals at the moment. He is not a man who is much interested in experimental styles, and, indeed, considers most of the modern literary innovations debasements. For him a story is a story in the old sense; it has a beginning, middle, and end, and the attitudes that the story exhibits are a matter of concern to him. To that degree, he is perhaps not a professional. He is most certainly not a formalist, and would, I am sure, wish his work burned if he thought that its influence were pernicious. Morality, God, life are more important to him than Art. And perhaps that is one of the reasons he writes so well.

Singer's first significant work is *Satan in Goray* which was composed before he was thirty. The book is set in the seventeenth century, some sixteen years after the terrifying Chmeilnicki pogrom. The year is 1665, and as Jacob Sloan, the translator of the work points out in his introduction, "Jewish expectations of the advent of their Messiah are at their height. For this is the year that cabalists, through numerological calculations, based on esoteric Biblical texts, have designated as the long awaited 'end of days.' Moreover, the times seem extraordinarily propitious for the redemption of the dispersed children of Israel from the sufferings of their Exile." As Sloan goes on to point out, 100,000 Jews had perished during the years from 1648 to 1658. "The peasant uprisings of this decade, and the bloody reprisals exacted by the Polish magnates appear to the Jews of 1665 to presage the ultimate battle of Armageddon, at the conclusion of which (the spent defeat of both hosts) tradition had it that the true Messiah would appear."

A Messiah was fervently desired, and so a Messiah did appear, namely one Sabbatai Zevi, an Oriental Jew who preached to the Jews of Europe and the Near East the imminent end of their captivity and a return to the paradise of the Holy Lands.

However, Singer does not deal with Sabbatai Zevi, himself, but with certain disciples of the prophet who come to the small Polish hamlet of Goray. The town, almost totally destroyed in the massacre, is being rebuilt under the direction of its pious, energetic leader, Rabbi Bemish. One day a rabbinical legate, a Jew from Yemen,

appears in town. But let me read you Singer himself.
"Suddenly the sharp clanging of a bell was heard in
the marketplace, and a sleigh drove up. A man with a
snow covered beard and long earlocks got out. He was
wearing a red turban and a fur coat turned inside out.
Darting fiery glances everywhere with his black eyes he
asked, 'Where is the study house?'

"The newcomer appeared in the holy place between
the afternoon and evening prayers. His arrival created
a sensation. He stopped at the threshold where he pulled
off his felt shoes and stood in stockinged feet. Afterwards, he removed his outer garment, revealing a long
smock, black-striped like a prayer shawl, and girdled
about with an embroidered sash. Washing his hands and
feet for a long time at the copper water tap, the newcomer turned his face to the eastern wall, and cried out
in a trembling voice: 'Judeans, I come to bring you good
tidings! From Jerusalem our holy city!'

"The newcomer's arrival immediately became known
in town, and a throng came running to the study house.
Womenfolk mingled with menfolk, young men and
girls stood up together on their reading stands and tables.
Everyone gaped and listened. The stranger spoke in a
broken voice, one that seemed to be full of tears:

" 'Judeans,' he said, 'I come from our holy land. I am
a pure-blooded Sephardi. I have been sent by my

brothers into the Exile to tell you that the Great Fish
that lurks in the river Nile has succumbed at the hands
of Sabbatai Zevi, our Messiah and holy King. . . . His
kingship will soon be revealed, and he will take the sultan's
crown from his head. . . . The Jews from the other
side of the river Sambation are ready and waiting for
the battle at Armageddon . . . The lion that dwelleth
on high will descend from Heaven, in his mouth a seven-
headed scorpion. . . . With fire issuing from his nostrils, he will carry the Messiah into Jerusalem. Gather
your strength, O Judeans, and make yourselves ready!
. . . Happy is the man who shall live to see this!'

"The study house became so quiet that a solitary fly
could be heard buzzing, beating its wings against the
windows. Women wrung their hands, and from their
grimaces it was difficult to tell whether they were laughing or weeping. There was a sea of startled faces. The
crowd stirred, as when the ram's horn is blown on Rosh
Hashana. The legate looked about him."

I have read you so extensively from *Satan in Goray*
so as to give you some idea of the magnificence of the
prose even in translation. What it sounds like in Yiddish
I have no more idea than you do, but I am told by those
who know the language well that the English equivalent
of any Singer is inevitably a watering down. But as far
as I am concerned even the English will do. I am sure

you noticed while I was reading how quickly Singer builds the dramatic tensions. He is a master at picking out just the right detail to keep the texture rich while at the same time pushing the narrative on. The scene as it goes on leads into hysteria. Millennial enthusiasm conquers Goray and finally the powerful old Rabbi is expelled from town.

There is not time here to go into a detailed study of the novel's plot. The title of the book enunciates its fundamental vision. It is not the Messiah but Satan who has come to Goray. With the vanishing of the old Rabbi, lawlessness takes over. The town is ruled by the emissaries of the devil, and in the forefront is the epileptic girl Rechele who seems almost a materialization of Lilith. But after the debauchery and the meaningless rejoicing comes despair. The people are so improvident, so certain that they will spend the New Year in the Holy Lands transported there by a cloud, that they do not bother to prepare for the winter. The houses are used as kindling wood; the rebuilding that Rabbi Bemish had so well begun ceases. And finally one day comes the word of the apostasy of Sabbatai Zevi who, incapable of facing martyrdom, becomes a Turkish convert. Goray, stripped and naked, has accomplished its own destruction as efficiently as had Chmeilnicki sixteen years before.

The basic meaning of the story is, of course, obvious.

Man is in no position to live anticipating millennia. Such paradises are not to be found in this world and the "mystic" intuitions that lead to such beliefs are to be seen as radically evil. Man must live by the Law, though this is the more difficult way. Those who set themselves up as gods or Messiahs are legates from hell. In his book Singer draws no parallel with the various secular faiths that have arisen in the world since the decline of the religious hysteria of the seventeenth century. But, of course, the fundamental philosophy enunciated in *Satan in Goray* applies to them also. Whether it is men speaking for God or for modern altruism would make little difference to Singer. The proposal of an impossible ideal will only enervate the possible, and the outcome will be not a better but a worse world.

It is for this reason that Singer is generally regarded as a pessimist. His expectations are not high. Man is not perfectible. His capacity for sin is infinite. But this does not mean that Singer is agnostic. On the contrary, existence is good, and it is meaningful. If man is on trial, he is not undergoing Kafka's trial in which life is reduced to mere anxiety. In Singer's cosmos, there are good days and bad days, happy moments and sad ones. Even in crisis the universe is recognizable as the one presented to common sense. In other words he does not stylize reality away. And indeed as he has grown older, much of the unrelieved intensity of his first vision has been modulated. *Satan in Goray* moves relentlessly. It is somewhat tight-lipped; no smiles are permitted. I should like to read you the opening of *Gimpel the Fool* which was translated by Saul Bellow and has been called by the *Times Literary Supplement* "the greatest schlemiel story in literature."

"I am Gimpel the Fool. I don't think myself a fool. On the contrary. But that's what folks call me. They gave me the name while I was still in school. I have seven names in all: imbecile, donkey, flax-head, dope, glump, ninny, and fool. The last name stuck. What did my foolishness consist of? I was easy to take in. They said, 'Gimpel, you know the rabbi's wife has been brought to childbed?' So I skipped school. Well, it turned out to be a lie. How was I supposed to know? She hadn't had a big belly. But I never looked at her belly. Was that really so foolish? The gang laughed and hee-hawed, stomped and danced and chanted a good-night prayer. And instead of the raisins they give when a woman's lying in, they stuffed my hand full of goat turds. I was no weakling. If I slapped someone he'd see all the way to Cracow. But I'm really not a slugger by nature. I think to myself: Let it pass. So they take advantage of me."

It is obvious from this small sampling how much more

colloquial Singer's prose is here than in *Satan in Goray*. It is clear too that humor has begun to function, and as a matter of fact, "Gimpel the Fool" is a hilariously funny story. The humor is savage, but wonderfully in keeping with the theme. Gimpel is the perpetually deceived, the butt of all jokes, and is finally married off to the town whore whom he is told is a spotless virgin. But at this point we will let Gimpel take over again.

"She gave birth to a boy. Friday at the synagogue the sexton stood up before the Ark, pounded on the reading table, and announced, 'The wealthy Reb Gimpel invites the congregation to a feast in honor of the birth of a son.' The whole House of Prayer rang with laughter. My face was flaming. But there was nothing I could do. After all, I *was* responsible for the circumcision honors and rituals.

"Half the town came running. You couldn't wedge another soul in. Women brought peppered chick-peas, and there was a keg of beer from the tavern. I ate and drank as much as anyone, . . . and I named the boy after my father, may he rest in peace. When all were gone and I was left with my wife alone, she thrust her head through the bed-curtain and called me to her.

" 'Gimpel,' said she, 'why are you so silent? Has your ship gone and sunk?'

" 'What shall I say?' I answered. 'A fine thing you've

done to me! If my mother had known of it she'd have died a second time.'

"She said, 'Are you crazy or what?'

" 'How can you make such a fool,' I said, 'of one who should be the lord and master?'

" 'What's the matter with you?' she said. 'What have you taken it into your head to imagine?'

"I saw that I must speak bluntly and openly. 'Do you think this is the way to use an orphan?' I said. 'You have borne a bastard.'

"She answered, 'Drive this foolishness out of your head. The child is yours.'

" 'How can he be mine?' I argued. 'He was born seventeen weeks after the wedding.'

"She told me then that he was premature. I said, 'Isn't he a little too premature?' She said, she had had a grand-mother who carried just as short a time and she resembled this grandmother of hers as one drop of water does another. She swore to it with such oaths that you would have believed a peasant at the fair if he had used them. To tell the plain truth, I didn't believe her; but when I talked it over the next day with the schoolmaster he told me that the very same thing had happened to Adam and Eve: Two they went up to bed, and four they descended."

The comic inventiveness of this passage is astounding.

And the fascinating part, of course, is that Gimpel is not taken in. He is both deceived and not deceived. The fact is he wants to be deceived because Gimpel is totally lacking in malice. But the world that puts upon Gimpel is full of malice and wants to deceive. It, itself, is never deceived; it is clearheaded. Yet its clearheadedness leads to cruelty and evil. It is loveless and Gimpel loves. Gradually we see that the whole story is a marvelous little parable of appearance and reality. Who is the deceived and who the deceiver? As Gimpel says very close to the end of the story, "No doubt the world is entirely an imaginary world, but it is only once removed from the true world." A very Platonic statement, and one whose implications can turn the clearheaded realists into the fools, and Gimpel, whose brain is small but whose heart is large, into more than the fool that he is on earth. In Singer's story, Gimpel is a holy fool. He is certainly not Singer's ideal of human perfection. The saintly rabbis who are to be found in several of his stories are closer to his ideal than is Gimpel.

I wish we had time to go through more of Singer's work and I could detail at length the fate of the young woman who is seduced by a minor demon through a mirror in the attic, and the story of the gentleman who comes from Cracow to become the beneficiary of the town of Frampol, as well as the dramatic undoing of

Peltke the Wifekiller, but it is obvious that the whole of Singer cannot be presented in half an hour. Before I finish I should like to say, however, a few words about *The Magician of Lublin* since in many ways this, his latest book, sums up much that he has been saying for a number of years. The principal character in the novel is Yasha Mazur, a rather Houdini-like character whose skill as a conjurist and illusionist has brought him fame and wealth. Yasha is a Jew who has given up his religion but remains married to a woman who has stayed in the faith. But though Yasha does not believe in the old faith he is a constant speculator on the divine. He is a God-driven man who cannot quite believe. He is also a man of enormous appetites, and while on the road carries on a series of love-affairs with women half out of sensuality and half out of boredom. The story happens at the end of the nineteenth century and we can see in Yasha the representative of modern man as we know him.

Yasha is sensitive and kind, impulsive and undisciplined. He is ambitious and entertaining, but despite all his virtues he is lawless. He has a hankering for the divine but he is out of touch with the divine and as he moves through the world he spreads havoc. The destructive element in Yasha is not immediately discernible; it is not until he becomes involved with a Christian widow in Warsaw that the full implications of his actions become evident. Yasha is finally saved; but he can only be saved through self-imprisonment. As in all of Singer's works, so here most clearly, Singer, although he is in no sense a puritan and nowhere denigrates the pleasures of life, looks with extreme suspicion on the unguarded instincts. He is in my opinion no "Naysayer," but he is too sophisticated to fall for any of the innumerable modern panaceas. Neither sexual freedom, nor ownership of the means of production by the workers, nor free assembly, nor the elimination of racial or religious discrimination will save man. In *Satan in Goray* the meaningful work of Rabbi Bemish was destroyed by millennial dreams. In *The Magician of Lublin* Yasha Mazur finds sanctuary by walling himself up. Even walled away from the world, Yasha does not attain peace. For Singer is no sentimentalist; absolute peace is only reserved for the dead. The living must struggle with their desires and must grope for meaning. As Singer wrote in an article, "There are only God-seekers; there are no God-finders." But for Singer, God-seeking is of the essence if man is not to brutalize himself.